Printed at the Mathematical Centre at Amsterdam, 49, 2nd Boerhaavestraat, The Netherlands.

The Mathematical Centre, founded the 11th of February 1946, is a non-profit institution aiming at the promotion of pure mathematics and its applications, and is sponsored by the Netherlands Government through the Netherlands Organization for the Advancement of Pure Research (Z.W.O.) and the Central Organization for Applied Scientific Research in the Netherlands (T.N.O.), by the Municipality of Amsterdam and by several industries.

MATHEMATICAL CENTRE TRACTS
19

MATHEMATICAL CENTRE TRACTS
19

SOME PROPERTIES RELATED TO COMPACTNESS

BY

J. VAN DER SLOT

MATHEMATISCH CENTRUM AMSTERDAM
1968

ERRATA

ge line

.2 5 *for* X *read* $\mathfrak{S}$

for $= S$ *read* $\supset S$

.6 2 *for* $X = \{Y \setminus \{p\} \mid p \in Y \setminus X\}$ *read* $X = \bigcap\{Y \setminus \{p\} \mid p \in Y \setminus X\}$

31 2 below *for* of $\mathfrak{U}_1$ *read* of $\mathfrak{U}$

34 9 *for* in X *read* in Y

39 16 *for* X *read* $\mathfrak{S}$

for $= S$ *read* $\supset S$

40 13 *for* AARTS and DE GROOT [1,13] *read* AARTS [1]

40 24 *for* SKETCH OF THE PROOF *read* For the case that $\mathfrak{S}$ satisfies the stronger regularity condition defined on page 47 we give the following SKETCH OF THE PROOF (for the general case see [1] p. 17).

8 Replace the proof of $1 \Rightarrow 2$ by the following elementary proof.

PROOF. Let $\mathfrak{S}_1$ be a maximal centered system of members of $\mathfrak{S}$ with the countable intersection property. Let $\mathfrak{U}'$ be the collection consisting of all $U \in \mathfrak{U}$ for which there exists $S \in \mathfrak{S}$ such that $S \subset U$. Finally, let $\mathfrak{U}_1$ be a maximal centered family of members of $\mathfrak{U}$ that contains $\mathfrak{U}'$. We will show that $\overline{\mathfrak{U}}_1$ has c.i.p. whence it follows that $\bigcap \overline{\mathfrak{U}}_1 \neq \emptyset$ and also $\bigcap \mathfrak{S}_1 \neq \emptyset$. Assume that, on the contrary, $\{\overline{U}_i \mid i=1,2,\ldots\}$ is a countable subcollection of $\overline{\mathfrak{U}}_1$ with empty intersection. Since $\mathfrak{S}$ is complemented, by virtue of the countability condition for $\mathfrak{S}$, there exists a countable refinement $\{S_n \mid n=1,2,\ldots\}$ of the cover $\{X \setminus \overline{U}_i \mid i=1,2,\ldots\}$. By maximality of $\mathfrak{S}_1$ there are indices m and j such that $S_m \in \mathfrak{S}_1$ and $S_m \cap \overline{U}_j = \emptyset$. Let (S_1, S_2) be a two element screening of the pair $(S_m, \overline{U}_j)$ $(S_1, S_2 \in \mathfrak{S})$. Then, by definition, $X \setminus S_2$ is a member of $\mathfrak{U}_1$ which does not intersect U_j. This is impossible, and it proves the first part of the theorem.

5 25 *for* [12] J. DE GROOT and J.M. AARTS *read* [12] J.M. AARTS

CONTENTS

INTRODUCTION

In this thesis our aim is to give a systematic study of a few topological generalizations of compactness in Hausdorff spaces. Our main interest lies in generalizations that are related to compactness with respect to heredity for topological operations, as the taking of closed subsets and the forming of topological products. In particular, much effort is made to obtain an intrinsic characterization of realcompactness [10] (i.e., a characterization of realcompactness in which we do not use explicitly the special properties of real-valued continuous functions).

When introducing a property of topological spaces, it is natural to ask if the property is inherited by closed subsets, open subsets and topological products. In general, it is difficult to decide whether or not a property satisfies any of these three conditions, nevertheless, a criterion which gives a decisive answer in a few cases is obtained in Chapter I. The following result is proved (theorem 1.1.3.): For a productive property of Hausdorff spaces the condition of being open-hereditary and closed-hereditary is equivalent with the condition of being hereditary. It is an open question whether or not the Hausdorff condition is essential.

Also in the first chapter, we investigate those properties which are closed-hereditary and productive. Let $\mathfrak{P}$ be a property of topological spaces. A $\mathfrak{P}$ *-extension* of a space X is a space with property $\mathfrak{P}$ which contains X as a dense subspace; a $\mathfrak{P}$ -extension γX of a space X is called *maximal* if each continuous map of X into any space Y satisfying $\mathfrak{P}$ has a continuous extension over γX. A space is called $\mathfrak{P}$ *-regular* if it is homeomorphic with a subspace of a product of spaces each of them satisfying $\mathfrak{P}$. We have the following result (theorem 1.2.1.): A necessary and sufficient condition for a property of Hausdorff spaces to allow maximal $\mathfrak{P}$ - extensions for all $\mathfrak{P}$ -regular spaces is that $\mathfrak{P}$ is closed-hereditary and productive.

This result was obtained independently by HERRLICH [15]. See also [29] and [17].

Now, let $\mathfrak{P}$ be the property of compactness. Then a $\mathfrak{P}$-extension is simply a compactification. Furthermore, it is well-known that every completely regular space X has a (unique) maximal $\mathfrak{P}$-extension (i.e. maximal compactification). Namely, the Čech-Stone compactification βX satisfies all required conditions. Maximal $\mathfrak{P}$-extensions have also been constructed for the properties realcompactness (Hewitt extension υX, see [10]), E-compactness (ENGELKING and MROWKA [5]), compactness & zerodimensionality (BANASCHEWSKI [3]), and for k-compactness and m-ultracompactness (resp., [15] and [29]). Our general result includes all of the preceding extension methods as special cases.

In Chapter II we introduce two new topological properties. The first one, called basiscompactness, is open-hereditary, productive, and is possessed by all locally compact Hausdorff spaces. Basiscompactness is defined by imposing a compactness condition on a base for the topology: If $\mathfrak{U}$ is an open base for a space X, then X is called *basiscompact relative* to $\mathfrak{U}$ if for each centered family $\mathfrak{U}_1 \subset \mathfrak{U}$ the collection $\overline{\mathfrak{U}_1}$ has non empty intersection. A space X is called *basiscompact* if there exists an open base $\mathfrak{U}$ such that X is basiscompact relative to $\mathfrak{U}$. Basiscompactness is a stronger version of subcompactness introduced in [11], but it is weaker than cocompactness introduced in [12]. In metric spaces these three properties are equivalent, and give an intrinsic characterization of the notion of topological completeness. We also prove that basiscompactness is invariant for a special kind of mapping: every perfect irreducible image of a basiscompact space is basiscompact (theorem 2.1.6.). It is unknown whether or not such a mapping theorem exists for the notions of subcompactness and cocompactness.

The second topological property which we introduce in Chapter II is defined by imposing a compactness condition on a closed subbase: If $\mathfrak{S}$ is a subbase for the closed sets of a space X, then X is called *m-ultracompact relative to* $\mathfrak{S}$ (m being an infinite cardinal number) provided that each ultrafilter $\mathfrak{F}$ in X for which $\mathfrak{F} \cap \mathfrak{S}$ satisfies the m-intersection property (i.e. each subcollection of cardinal $< m$ has non empty intersection) is convergent. A space is called *m-ultracompact* iff it is m-ultracompact relative to some closed subbase for its topology, or, equivalently, if it is m-ultracompact relative to the (sub)base consisting of all closed sets. m-ultracompactness resembles, to some extent, the property of k-compactness introduced by HERRLICH [15]: it is closed-hereditary and productive, is possessed by all compact spaces, and $\aleph_1$-ultracompactness coincides with realcompactness in countably paracompact normal spaces (for the definition of realcompactness see [10]). We also prove that m-ultracompactness is a fitting property, i.e., if f is a perfect map of a space X onto a space Y, then both or neither of X and Y must be m-ultracompact (theorem 2.2.6.).

If X is $\aleph_1$-ultracompact relative to some subbase $\mathfrak{S}$, then it is natural to ask what separation conditions should be put on $\mathfrak{S}$ in order that X becomes a realcompact completely regular space. In the same way we can ask what conditions we should put on a space X which is basiscompact relative to a base $\mathfrak{U}$ for its open subsets in order that X becomes a compact Hausdorff space. The second question is easy to solve. A base $\mathfrak{S}$ for the closed subsets of a space X satisfies the *condition of base-regularity* if for each member $S \in \mathfrak{S}$ and point $p \notin S$, there exist $S_1, S_2 \in \mathfrak{S}$ such that $S_1 \cup S_2 = X$, $p \notin S_2$, $S \cap S_1 = \emptyset$. It is easy to prove that a T_1-space is compact Hausdorff if and only if it is basiscompact relative to a base $\mathfrak{U}$ for which the corresponding closed base $\mathfrak{S} = \{X \setminus U | U \in \mathfrak{U}\}$ satisfies the condition of base-regularity.

Now, let X be a space which is $\aleph_1$-ultracompact relative to a closed subbase $\mathfrak{S}$. We must find extra conditions for $\mathfrak{S}$ such that the space X becomes a realcompact completely regular space. This is certainly the case when $\mathfrak{S}$ is the family of all zerosets of X (see [10] page 153). But we are looking for intrinsic conditions for $\mathfrak{S}$! Two subsets A and B of a topological space X are *screened* by a finite collection of subsets $\mathfrak{C}$ iff no member of $\mathfrak{C}$ intersects both A and B. A subbase $\mathfrak{S}$ for the closed sets of a space X satisfies the *regularity condition* (*condition of subbase-regularity*) provided that for each $S \in \mathfrak{S}$ and $x \notin S$, there exist subsets $S_1, \ldots, S_n$ of X such that $\cup \{S_i | i=1,2,\ldots,n\} = S$ and each pair (x,S_i) is screened by a finite subcollection of $\mathfrak{S}$. $\mathfrak{S}$ satisfies the *normality condition* (*condition of subbase-normality*) iff each two disjoint members of $\mathfrak{S}$ are screened by a finite cover of X consisting of members of $\mathfrak{S}$. $\mathfrak{S}$ satisfies the *countability condition* if each countable cover of X by members of $\{X \setminus S | S \in \mathfrak{S}\}$ has a countable refinement by members of $\mathfrak{S}$. Now we have the following result (theorem 3.1.8.): A T_1-space X is a realcompact completely regular space if and only if it is $\aleph_1$-ultracompact relative to a closed subbase which satisfies the regularity, normality and countability conditions. Note (see 3.1.4.) that for such a subbase $\mathfrak{S}$, the condition of being $\aleph_1$-ultracompact relative to $\mathfrak{S}$ is equivalent with the condition that each maximal centered family of members of $\mathfrak{S}$ with the countable intersection property has non empty intersection. If we work now within the complementary framework of collections of open sets and open covers, then it follows that a sufficient condition for realcompactness of a space is presented by the existence of a "nice" open subbase with the Lindelöf property (i.e. each cover by members of the subbase has a countable subcover). This answers a question which was raised by J. DE GROOT. The problem whether realcompactness is equivalent to the existence of such a "Lindelöf subbase" still remains unsolved.

In [12] the conditions of subbase-regularity and subbase-normality were introduced. In [1] AARTS showed that for each T_1-space X, which has a closed subbase $\mathfrak{S}$ satisfying the conditions of subbase-regularity and subbase-normality, there exists a Hausdorff compactification $\beta(\mathfrak{S})X$ such that the closures in $\beta(\mathfrak{S})X$ of the members of $\mathfrak{S}$ form a closed subbase for $\beta(\mathfrak{S})X$. See also [13], [7] and [31].

In Chapter III we obtain a similar theorem for the realcompact case:

THEOREM. Let X be a T_1-space and $\mathfrak{S}$ be a closed subbase for X which satisfies the regularity, normality, and countability conditions. Then there exists a completely regular realcompactification $\upsilon(\mathfrak{S})X$ of X with the following properties:

1. The closures in $\upsilon(\mathfrak{S})X$ of the members of $\mathfrak{S}$ form a closed subbase for $\upsilon(\mathfrak{S})X$ and satisfies the regularity, normality, and countability conditions. Each maximal centered family of this collection satisfying c.i.p. has non empty intersection in $\upsilon(\mathfrak{S})X$.

2. If $\{S_i \mid i=1,2,\ldots\}$ is a countable subcollection of $\mathfrak{S}$ with empty intersection, then their closures in $\upsilon(\mathfrak{S})X$ have empty intersection in $\upsilon(\mathfrak{S})X$.

In Chapter III we also obtain a result which shows that our realcompactification $\upsilon(\mathfrak{S})X$ is maximal in a certain respect.

THEOREM. Let X and Y be T_1-spaces, and suppose that $\mathfrak{S}$ and $\mathfrak{T}$ are closed subbases for X and Y, respectively, which satisfy the regularity, normality, and countability conditions. If f is a (continuous) map of X into Y such that $f^{-1}(T) \in \mathfrak{S}$ for each $T \in \mathfrak{T}$, then there exists a continuous extension of f which carries $\upsilon(\mathfrak{S})X$ into $\upsilon(\mathfrak{T})Y$.

The final results in Chapter III are applications of the obtained realcompactification method. As a typical example we have the following result: Let $\{X_\alpha \mid \alpha \in A\}$ be a collection of topological spaces and $X = \Pi\{X_\alpha \mid \alpha \in A\}$. If for $\alpha \in A$, $\mathfrak{S}_\alpha$ is a closed subbase of X_α which satisfies the regularity, normality, and countability conditions, then the subbase $\mathfrak{S}$ of X consisting of the sets $\pi_\alpha^{-1}(C)$, where $C \in \mathfrak{S}_\alpha$ $(\alpha \in A)$, also satisfies these conditions and $\upsilon(\mathfrak{S})X$ is homeomorphic with $\Pi\{\upsilon(\mathfrak{S}_\alpha)X_\alpha \mid \alpha \in A\}$.

Here I wish to express my gratitude to the Mathematical Centre, Amsterdam, which gave me the opportunity to carry on the investigations which are dealt with in this treatise. I am indebted to Dr. G.A. Jensen who carefully read the manuscript and corrected it, especially in its English expression. Here I wish to thank also Mrs. H. Roqué-de Hoyer and Mr. D. Zwarst for typing and printing the manuscript.

CONVENTIONS

Throughout this thesis all spaces are considered to be T_1-spaces, whereas the results are only of practical use for Hausdorff spaces.

"Collection", "family" and "system" are synonymous for "set", $\in$ denotes membership. The empty set will be denoted by $\emptyset$.

The symbols $\subset$ and $\supset$ mean ordinary inclusion between sets, they do not exclude the possibility of equality. If A and B are sets, then $A \setminus B$ will denote the set of points of A which do not belong to B.

Mappings will be considered as left operators and are written on the left of the argument. If f is a mapping of X into Y and $A \subset X$, $B \subset Y$, then $f(A) = \{f(a) \mid a \in A\}$, $f^{-1}(B) = \{x \in X \mid f(x) \in B\}$.

Italic latin letters stand for cardinals, $\aleph_0$ stands for the cardinal number of a countable set, $\aleph$ denotes the cardinal of the continuum.

The closure of a set A in a space X will be denoted by $\overline{A}^X$ or simply $\overline{A}$, the interior of A in X by A°.

Collections of subsets of a space are indicated by German letters; if $\mathfrak{U}$ is a family of subsets of a space X, then the symbol $\overline{\mathfrak{U}}^X$ is used to denote the collection of all $\overline{U}^X$ for which $U \in \mathfrak{U}$. The union and intersection of a family of sets $\mathfrak{U}$ will be denoted by $\cup\,\mathfrak{U}$ or $\cap\,\mathfrak{U}$, respectively. Sometimes we are concerned with indexed collections of sets, like $\{X_\alpha \mid \alpha \in A\}$. The union, intersection etc. is then simply denoted by $\cup\,\{X_\alpha \mid \alpha \in A\}$, $\cap\,\{X_\alpha \mid \alpha \in A\}$ etc.

If X is a space, then an *open (sub)base* of X is a (sub)base for the open sets of X; a *closed (sub)base* of X is a (sub)base for the closed sets of X. A subset Z of X is called a *zeroset* of X if there exists a real-valued continuous function f on X such that $Z = \{x \in X \mid f(x) = 0\}$. If X is completely regular, then the collection of zerosets of X is a closed base of X (see [10] for more information).

CHAPTER I

INVARIANCES OF TOPOLOGICAL PROPERTIES

1. HEREDITARY PROPERTIES

1.1.1. Recall that a property $\mathfrak{P}$ of topological spaces is called *productive* iff each product of an arbitrary collection of spaces having $\mathfrak{P}$, also has property $\mathfrak{P}$; it is called *hereditary* (respectively, *closed-hereditary*, *open-hereditary*) if each subspace (respectively closed subspace, open subspace) of a space with $\mathfrak{P}$ also has $\mathfrak{P}$.

1.1.2. LEMMA. Let $\mathfrak{P}$ be a property of T_2-spaces which is closed-hereditary and productive. If $\{X_\alpha \mid \alpha \in A\}$ is a collection of subsets of a T_2-space Y and if each X_α satisfies the property $\mathfrak{P}$, then $D = \cap \{X_\alpha \mid \alpha \in A\}$ satisfies the property $\mathfrak{P}$.

PROOF. Let $X = \Pi\{X_\alpha \mid \alpha \in A\}$ and let $\Delta \subset X$ be given by $\Delta = \{x \in X \mid \pi_\alpha(x) = \pi_\beta(x), \forall \alpha,\beta \in A\}$ (here π_α is the natural projection of X onto X_α). Define a mapping f of D onto Δ by the conditions $\pi_\alpha(f(p)) = p$, $\forall \alpha \in A$. f is continuous, since the map f followed by projection π_α is the inclusion map of D into X_α. Moreover, if U is an open set of D then there exists an open set U' of Y such that $U' \cap D = U$ which implies $f(U) = \pi_\alpha^{-1}(U' \cap X_\alpha) \cap \Delta$ for each α. It follows that $f(U)$ is open in Δ and consequently f is a homeomorphism. So it remains to show that Δ has property $\mathfrak{P}$. X has property $\mathfrak{P}$ since each X_α has property $\mathfrak{P}$ and $\mathfrak{P}$ is productive.By the Hausdorff property of Y it follows that Δ is closed in X, so Δ also has property $\mathfrak{P}$ since $\mathfrak{P}$ is closed-hereditary.

1.1.3. THEOREM. (See also [17] and [29]). Let $\mathfrak{P}$ be a property of T_2-spaces which is productive. Then the following conditions are equivalent:

(i) $\mathfrak{P}$ is open-hereditary and closed-hereditary,

(ii) $\mathfrak{P}$ is hereditary.

PROOF. (i) $\Rightarrow$ (ii). Let X be a subset of a space Y with property $\mathfrak{P}$. We have $X = \{Y \setminus \{p\} \mid p \in Y \setminus X\}$, i.e., X is an intersection of open subspaces of Y. By assumption each open subset of Y has property $\mathfrak{P}$ and by the preceding lemma each intersection of spaces satisfying $\mathfrak{P}$ also has $\mathfrak{P}$. Consequently X has property $\mathfrak{P}$.
(ii) $\Rightarrow$ (i). This is immediately clear.

1.1.4. An easy consequence of the foregoing theorem is that if $\mathfrak{P}$ is a property of T_2-spaces which is open hereditary, closed-hereditary, productive, and is possessed by all compact T_2-spaces, then $\mathfrak{P}$ is possessed by every completely regular space.

This corollary can serve as a test for deciding whether or not some property of T_2-spaces is inherited by open subsets, closed subsets or topological products. Consider the properties C = compactness, LC = local compactness, CC = cocompactness [12], K = being a k-space [23], and RC = realcompactness [10]. The following table is filled out + or -, depending on whether the property at the head of the column is or is not of the sort listed on the left.

	C	LC	CC	K	RC
closed-hereditary	+	+	-	+	+
open-hereditary	-	+	+	+	-
productive	+	-	+	-	+

If we consider, for instance, the property of being a k-space, then it is easy to see that this property is closed-hereditary and open-hereditary (if we restrict ourselves to Hausdorff spaces). Moreover, each (locally) compact T_2-space is a k-space. However, we known that there exist completely regular spaces which are not k-spaces. Hence the property of being a k-space is not productive.

1.1.5. PROBLEM. Up to the present we have not succeeded in constructing a property of T_1-spaces which is open-hereditary, closed-hereditary and productive, and which is not a hereditary property. Thus the question remains open whether or not, in 1.1.3., the Hausdorff condition is essential.

2. MAXIMAL $\mathfrak{P}$ -EXTENSIONS

1.2.1. Recall that if $\mathfrak{P}$ is a topological property, then a $\mathfrak{P}$ -*extension* of a space X is a space with property $\mathfrak{P}$ which contains X as a dense subspace. A $\mathfrak{P}$ -extension γX of a space X is called *maximal* iff each continuous map of X into any space Y satisfying $\mathfrak{P}$ has a continuous extension over γX.
A maximal $\mathfrak{P}$ -extension γX of a space X is uniquely determined (i.e. determined up to a homeomorphism) by X, and we have $\gamma X = X$ if and only if X has property $\mathfrak{P}$.

A space is called $\mathfrak{P}$ *-regular* iff it is homeomorphic with a subspace of a product of spaces each of them satisfying $\mathfrak{P}$.

LEMMA. If ϕ is a continuous map of a T_2-space Y into a space Z whose restriction to a dense set X is a homeomorphism, then ϕ carries $Y \setminus X$ into $Z \setminus \phi(X)$.

PROOF. E.g. [10] page 92.

THEOREM. [1] If $\mathfrak{P}$ is a property of T_2-spaces, then the following statements are equivalent:

(a) Each $\mathfrak{P}$ -regular space possesses a maximal $\mathfrak{P}$ -extension,

(b) $\mathfrak{P}$ is productive and closed-hereditary.

---

[1] This result was obtained independently by HERRLICH [15]. See also [17] and [29]. Parts of it are contained in KENNISON [24] and HUŠEK [20] (see the notes on page 19 of this thesis).

PROOF. (a) $\Rightarrow$ (b). Let $\mathfrak{P}$ be a topological property which satisfies the condition (a).

First. $\mathfrak{P}$ is productive: Let $\{X_\alpha | \alpha \in A\}$ be a collection of spaces having $\mathfrak{P}$ and $X = \Pi\{X_\alpha | \alpha \in A\}$. By assumption X possesses a maximal $\mathfrak{P}$-extension γX such that each projection map $\pi_\alpha : X \to X_\alpha$ has a continuous extension $\bar{\pi}_\alpha : \gamma X \to X_\alpha$. Let $j: \gamma X \to X$ be defined by the conditions $(j(x))_\alpha = \bar{\pi}_\alpha(x)$ $(\alpha \in A)$. It is easy to see that j is the identity on X, hence by the preceding lemma $\gamma X \setminus X = \emptyset$, i.e., $\gamma X = X$. Consequently, X has property $\mathfrak{P}$.

Second. $\mathfrak{P}$ is closed-hereditary: Let X be a closed subset of a space Y satisfying $\mathfrak{P}$. The inclusion map i of X into Y has a continuous extension i^* which carries γX into Y (γX being a maximal $\mathfrak{P}$-extension of X). By the preceding lemma, the preimage of the closed set X of Y under i^* is X; hence X is closed in γX, i.e. $\gamma X = X$. It follows that X has property $\mathfrak{P}$.

(b) $\Rightarrow$ (a). Let $\mathfrak{P}$ be a topological property which is productive and closed-hereditary, and let X be a $\mathfrak{P}$-regular space. Denote by $\mathcal{M}$ the class of all spaces with property $\mathfrak{P}$ which contain a continuous image of X as a dense subspace. By identifying homeomorphic copies, $\mathcal{M}$ becomes a set with cardinality $\leqq \exp\exp |X|$. For each $Y \in \mathcal{M}$, let $C(X,Y)$ be the set of all continuous mappings of X into Y. For $f \in C(X,Y)$, let $\pi_{(Y,f)}$ be the (Y,f)-th projection of the product space $P = \Pi\{Y^{C(X,Y)} | Y \in \mathcal{M}\}$. There exists exactly one continuous map $i: X \to P$ with the property $\pi_{(Y,f)} \circ i = f$ for all projection maps $\pi_{(Y,f)}$. Since X is $\mathfrak{P}$-regular, i is a homeomorphism of X into P. Denote by γX the closure in P of $i(X)$. Then, by construction, γX is the desired maximal $\mathfrak{P}$-extension of X.

COROLLARY. If $\mathfrak{P}$ is a property of completely regular spaces, then the following statements are equivalent:

(a) $\mathfrak{P}$ is closed-hereditary, productive, and is possessed by all compact T_2-spaces.

(b) Every completely regular space possesses a maximal $\mathfrak{P}$-extension (which is completely regular).

PROOF. Substitute for $\mathfrak{P}$ in the preceding theorem the property $\mathfrak{P}$ & complete regularity.

1.2.2. NOTES. 1. If we take for $\mathfrak{P}$ the property of compactness, then (a) ⇒ (b) in this corollary is precisely the Čech-Stone extension theorem. If we take for $\mathfrak{P}$ the property of realcompactness then (a) ⇒ (b) immediately yields the existence of a maximal realcompactification υX for every completely regular space X (Hewitt extension theorem cf. [10]).

The above corollary can also be applied to get results of ENGELKING and MROWKA [5] on E-compactness, and of BANASCHEWSKI [3] on compactness and zerodimensionality. See also [15] and [29].

2. In [24] KENNISON defined the concept of $\mathfrak{P}$-reflection, which is more general than the concept of maximal $\mathfrak{P}$-extension. A space γX is called a $\mathfrak{P}$-reflection of a space X iff 1) γX is a space with property $\mathfrak{P}$, 2) there is a continuous map γ of X onto a dense subset of γX, 3) for every continuous map f of X into any space Y satisfying $\mathfrak{P}$, there exists a continuous map $\bar{f}\colon \gamma X \to Y$ with the property $\bar{f} \circ \gamma = f$. It is shown in [24] that under the hypothesis that $\mathfrak{P}$ is closed-hereditary and productive, there exists a $\mathfrak{P}$-reflection γX for each Hausdorff space X. See also [20], [17] and [16]. However, in [24] we get no information under what circumstances γX is a maximal $\mathfrak{P}$-extension of X.

3. The existence of maximal $\mathfrak{P}$-extensions may be reformulated in categorical language. Indeed, the construction of a maximal $\mathfrak{P}$-extension γX of a space X yields a covariant functor which is adjoint to the corresponding forgetfullfunctor (cf. [6] for the definition of category, functor, etc.).

1.2.3. If f is a continuous map of a space X onto a T_2-space Y, then it is well-known that the mapping $h\colon X \to X \times Y$ defined by $h(x) = (x, f(x))$ is a homeomorphism of X onto a closed subspace (usually called the graph of f) of $X \times Y$. The following lemma generalizes this result.

LEMMA. Let X and Y be topological spaces, f a continuous map of X onto Y, and A, B subsets of X and Y, respectively, such that $f^{-1}(B) = A$. If Y is a Hausdorff space then the mapping h defined by $h(x) = (x, f(x))$ is a homeomorphism of A onto a closed subspace of $X \times B$.

PROOF. It is easy to see that h is a homeomorphism of A into $X \times B$; hence it suffices to show that $h(A)$ is closed in $X \times B$. Let $g: X \times B \to Y \times B$ be defined by $g(x,y) = (f(x),y)$. Since Y is a Hausdorff space $D = \{(y,y) \mid y \in B\}$ is closed in $Y \times B$; hence $h(A) = g^{-1}(D)$ is closed in $X \times B$.

1.2.4. From the preceding lemma we derive the following result:

THEOREM. Let $\mathfrak{P}$ be a property of T_2-spaces which is inherited by closed subsets and invariant for the taking of finite topological products. If f is a continuous map from a space X with property $\mathfrak{P}$ onto a T_2-space Y, then the inverse image under f of each subset of Y with property $\mathfrak{P}$, also satisfies $\mathfrak{P}$.

1.2.5. Following the terminology used in [18] a property $\mathfrak{P}$ of topological spaces is called an *almost-fitting property* (respectively *fitting property*) if whenever f is a perfect [1)] map of a completely regular space X onto a completely regular space Y, then X has property $\mathfrak{P}$ if (respectively if and only if) Y has $\mathfrak{P}$.

Compactness, local compactness, paracompactness and countable paracompactness are examples of fitting properties (see [18]). Realcompactness is an example of an almost-fitting property.

---

1) A mapping f of a space X into a space Y will be called *perfect* if f is continuous, closed (the images of closed sets are closed) and the inverse images of points are compact.

The following theorem gives a criterion for deciding whether or not some property is an almost-fitting property.

THEOREM. Let $\mathfrak{P}$ be a property of topological spaces. Suppose that $\mathfrak{P}$ is closed-hereditary, and suppose that for every (completely regular) space Y satisfying $\mathfrak{P}$, the product of Y with any compact T_2-space has property $\mathfrak{P}$. Then $\mathfrak{P}$ is an almost-fitting property.

PROOF. Let Y be a completely regular space satisfying $\mathfrak{P}$ and f a perfect map of a completely regular space X onto Y. We must show that X has property $\mathfrak{P}$. Let $\overline{f}$ be the continuous extension of f which carries βX into βY (βX and βY denoting the Čech-Stone compactifications of X and Y, respectively). A well-known theorem of Henriksen and Isbell states that $\overline{f}^{-1}(Y) = X$ (see [18]). Hence by 1.2.3., X is homeomorphic with a closed subspace of $\beta X \times Y$. The theorem now follows from the assumptions we made on the property $\mathfrak{P}$.

1.2.6. If $\mathfrak{P}$ is a property defined on the class of completely regular spaces such that 1) every compact T_2-space has property $\mathfrak{P}$, 2) $\mathfrak{P}$ is closed-hereditary and productive, then we know from the corollary in 1.2.1. that every completely regular space X has a (uniquely determined) maximal $\mathfrak{P}$-extension γX. It is natural to ask whether or not it is true that γX is homeomorphic with a subspace of βX. We will now show that this is indeed the case.

For each continuous map f of X onto a dense subset of a space Y satisfying $\mathfrak{P}$, let $\overline{f}$ be the continuous extension of f which carries βX onto βY. Using the results in 1.1.2. and 1.2.4., it is easy to see that $\delta X = \bigcap \{\overline{f}^{-1}(Y) \mid Y \text{ has property } \mathfrak{P};\ f: X \to Y \text{ is continuous; } f(X) \text{ dense in } Y\}$ is a maximal $\mathfrak{P}$-extension of X which (by uniqueness of γX) is homeomorphic with γX.

1.2.7. THEOREM. Let $\mathfrak{P}$ be a property of completely regular spaces. Then the following conditions are equivalent:

(i) $\mathfrak{P}$ is possessed by every space consisting of a single point; $\mathfrak{P}$ is invariant for the taking of arbitrary (resp., finite, countable) intersections, and $\mathfrak{P}$ satisfies the condition that for each space Y satisfying $\mathfrak{P}$, the product of Y with any compact T_2-space has property $\mathfrak{P}$.

(ii) $\mathfrak{P}$ is closed-hereditary, productive (resp. invariant for finite, countable products), and is possessed by all compact T_2-spaces.

LEMMA. A property $\mathfrak{P}$ of completely regular spaces which is invariant for the taking of finite intersections and which is possessed by all compact T_2-spaces, is closed-hereditary.

PROOF. Let X be a space satisfying $\mathfrak{P}$ and Y a closed subspace of X. Let αX be a compact extension of X. $\overline{Y}^{\alpha X}$ and X are subsets of αX each satisfying $\mathfrak{P}$; hence their intersection, which equals Y, has property $\mathfrak{P}$.

PROOF OF THE THEOREM. (i) $\Rightarrow$ (ii). It is almost obvious that $\mathfrak{P}$ is possessed by all compact T_2-spaces. Indeed, if C is a compact T_2-space and S a space consisting of a single point, then by assumption $C \times S$ has property $\mathfrak{P}$ and this space is homeomorphic with C.

It follows from the preceding lemma that $\mathfrak{P}$ is closed-hereditary. Let us now show that $\mathfrak{P}$ is productive. Let $\{X_\alpha | \alpha \in A\}$ be a collection of completely regular spaces each of them satisfying $\mathfrak{P}$ (finite products and countable products are treated similarly), and let $X = \Pi\{X_\alpha | \alpha \in A\}$. Each projection map π_α of X onto X_α has a continuous extension π^*_α which carries βX into βX_α. For $\alpha \in A$, set $X(\alpha) = \pi^{*-1}_\alpha(X_\alpha)$. By 1.2.3. each $X(\alpha)$ is homeomorphic with a closed subspace of $\beta X \times X_\alpha$ and hence satisfies the property $\mathfrak{P}$. Our assumption yields that $X' = \cap \{X(\alpha) | \alpha \in A\}$ also satisfies $\mathfrak{P}$. But X is densely embedded in X' and the mapping $i^*: X' \to X$ defined by the conditions $(i^*(x))_\alpha = \pi^*_\alpha(x)$ $(\alpha \in A)$ is continuous and is the identity on X. Consequently it follows from the lemma in 1.2.1. that $X' = X$, i.e. X has property $\mathfrak{P}$.

(ii) $\Rightarrow$ (i). This follows at once from 1.1.2.

EXAMPLE. The property of paracompactness is not invariant for the taking of finite intersections.

Indeed, it is well-known that paracompactness is not invariant for the taking of finite topological products (see [23]). Hence, it follows that condition (ii) in 1.2.7. is not satisfied for the property of paracompactness. Since the product of a paracompact space and a compact T_2-space is again a paracompact space (see [27]), it follows from 1.2.7. that paracompactness is not invariant for the taking of finite intersections.

CHAPTER II

BASISCOMPACTNESS AND m-ULTRACOMPACTNESS

In the previous chapter we have seen that those topological properties which are closed-hereditary and productive are of special interest in the theory of extensions of mappings. In this chapter we shall introduce two new topological properties. The first one, called basiscompactness, is open-hereditary and productive. The second one, called m-ultracompactness, is closed-hereditary and productive. Both properties are defined by imposing a kind of compactness condition on a subbase for the topology. Later (Chapter III), it will be shown that by imposing certain separation conditions on the subbase, we obtain equivalence with compactness and realcompactness.

1. BASISCOMPACTNESS

In this section we introduce the notion of basiscompactness which is, roughly speaking, a weak form of compactness relative to some open base of the space. Basiscompactness is a stronger version of subcompactness introduced in [11], but it is weaker than cocompactness introduced in [12]. For metric spaces, these three properties are equivalent and give intrinsic characterizations of the notion of topological completeness (see also [8] and [30]). We also prove that basiscompactness is an invariant for perfect irreducible mappings (for the properties subcompactness and cocompactness this is an open question).

2.1.1. Let X be a space and $\mathfrak{U}$ an open base for its topology. X is called *basiscompact relative to* $\mathfrak{U}$ provided that for each centered system $\mathfrak{J}$ of members of $\mathfrak{U}$, the collection $\overline{\mathfrak{J}}$ has non empty intersection. A space X is called *basiscompact* if there exists a base $\mathfrak{U}$ for its topology such that X is basiscompact relative to $\mathfrak{U}$.

2.1.2. If X is a space which is basiscompact relative to some base $\mathfrak{U}$ for its open sets, then we can ask what separation conditions we should put on $\mathfrak{U}$ in order that X becomes a compact Hausdorff space.

A base $\mathfrak{S}$ for the closed sets of a space X is said to satisfy the *condition of base-regularity* if for each point p of X and $S \in \mathfrak{S}$ not containing p, there exists $S_1, S_2 \in \mathfrak{S}$ satisfying $S_1 \cup S_2 = X$, $p \notin S_2$, $S \cap S_1 = \emptyset$. (S_1, S_2) is called a *screening* of the pair (p,S). A base $\mathfrak{U}$ for the open sets of a space X is called *base-regular* if the corresponding closed base $\{X \setminus U | U \in \mathfrak{U}\}$ satisfies the condition of base-regularity.

Now we have the following result:

THEOREM. A T_1-space is a compact Hausdorff space if and only if it is basiscompact relative to a base which is base-regular.

PROOF. Sufficiency. Let X be a T_1-space and $\mathfrak{U}$ a base for the topology that is base-regular relative to which X is basiscompact. Set $\mathfrak{S} = \{X \setminus U | U \in \mathfrak{U}\}$. X is a Hausdorff space, for if p and q are different points of X, then by the T_1-property of X, there exists $S \in \mathfrak{S}$ such that $p \notin S$, $q \in S$, and a screening (S_1, S_2) of (p,S) by members of $\mathfrak{S}$. It follows that $X \setminus S_2$ and $X \setminus S_1$ are disjoint neighborhoods of p and q, respectively.

Now, let $\mathfrak{S}_1$ be a centered system of members of $\mathfrak{S}$. In order to prove the compactness of X, it is sufficient to prove that $\mathfrak{S}_1$ has non empty intersection in X. Define $\mathfrak{U}_1 \subset \mathfrak{U}$ by the condition $\mathfrak{U}_1 = \{U \in \mathfrak{U} | S \subset U$ for some $S \in \mathfrak{S}_1\}$. Obviously $\mathfrak{U}_1$ is a centered system of members of $\mathfrak{U}$; thus by basiscompactness of X relative to $\mathfrak{U}$, there exists $p \in \cap \overline{\mathfrak{U}}_1$ and hence it suffices to prove that $p \in \cap \mathfrak{S}_1$. Let us suppose that there exists $S \in \mathfrak{S}_1$ such that $p \notin S$. Since $\mathfrak{U}$ is base-regular, there exists a screening (S_1, S_2) of (p,S) by members of $\mathfrak{S}$. We have $S \subset X \setminus S_1$ and $p \notin \overline{X \setminus S_1}$. However, by construction, $X \setminus S_1 \in \mathfrak{U}_1$, thus $p \notin \cap \overline{\mathfrak{U}}_1$. This gives the desired contradiction.

Necessity: This is immediately clear!

PROPOSITION. A locally compact Hausdorff space is basiscompact relative to the base consisting of the open sets with compact closure.

PROOF. Obvious.

2.1.3. PROPOSITION. a. The property basiscompactness is inherited by arbitrary topological products. b. Each open subset of a regular basiscompact space is basiscompact. c. The property of basiscompactness is in general not inherited by closed subspaces.

PROOF. a. Suppose $\{X_\alpha | \alpha \in A\}$ is a collection of topological spaces, each X_α being basiscompact relative to a base $\mathfrak{U}_\alpha$. Let $X = \Pi\{X_\alpha | \alpha \in A\}$ and $\mathfrak{U}$ the base for the product topology of X consisting of all sets of the form $\Pi\{U_\alpha | \alpha \in A\}$ where U_α is a member of $\mathfrak{U}_\alpha$ for finitely many $\alpha \in A$ and $U_\alpha = X_\alpha$ for the remaining indices α. We will show that X is basiscompact relative to $\mathfrak{U}$. Let $\mathfrak{F}$ be a centered system of members of $\mathfrak{U}$. For each $\alpha \in A$, the collection $\{\pi_\alpha U | U \in \mathfrak{F}\}$ is a centered system of members of $\mathfrak{U}_\alpha$ [1] and consequently, there exists $p_\alpha \in \cap \{\overline{\pi_\alpha U} | U \in \mathfrak{F}\}$ for each α. Let p be the point of X whose α'th coordinate equals p_α. Then p is in the closures of the members of $\mathfrak{F}$.

b. If X is a regular space which is basiscompact relative to a base $\mathfrak{U}$ for its topology and if O is an open subset of X, then O is basiscompact relative to the base consisting of the elements of $\mathfrak{U}$ whose closures in X are contained in O.

c. [2] It follows from 2.1.2. and a that each product of real lines is basiscompact. Since the space Q of rational numbers is homeomorphic with a closed subspace of such a product (see [10]) it suffices to show that Q is not basiscompact. Suppose, on the contrary, that Q is basiscompact relative to a base $\mathfrak{U}$ for its open subsets. Take an

---

1) Without loss of generality we may suppose that $X_\alpha \in \mathfrak{U}_\alpha$ for each $\alpha \in A$.

2) Compare with [12].

enumeration $r_1, r_2, \ldots, r_n, \ldots$ of Q. Obviously there exists $U_1 \in \mathfrak{U}$ such that $r_1 \notin U_1$ while $U_1 \neq \emptyset$. If for $1 < k \leq n$ $U_k \in \mathfrak{U}$ is already defined such that $\overline{U}_k \subset U_{k-1}$, $r_k \notin U_k$, $U_k \neq \emptyset$ for $k = 2, \ldots, n$, then, take some rational number $r \in U_n$ which is not in $\{r_1, \ldots, r_{n+1}\}$ and let U_{n+1} be a member of $\mathfrak{U}$ with the properties $r \in U_{n+1} \subset \overline{U}_{n+1} \subset U_n$, $r_{n+1} \notin U_{n+1}$. The so constructed collection $\{U_n | n=1,2,\ldots\}$ is a centered system of members of $\mathfrak{U}$ and $\cap\{\overline{U}_n | n=1,2,\ldots\} = \cap \{U_n | n=1,2,\ldots\} = \emptyset$. This contradicts the assumption that Q is basiscompact relative to $\mathfrak{U}$.

2.1.4. PROPOSITION. Every basiscompact space is basiscompact relative to a base which is closed under finite unions. In fact, if X is basiscompact relative to $\mathfrak{U}$ then X is also basiscompact relative to $\mathfrak{U}^{\vee}$ (i.e. the collection of subsets of X which are finite unions of members of $\mathfrak{U}$).

PROOF. Suppose, on the contrary, that there is a centered system $\mathfrak{F} \subset \mathfrak{U}^{\vee}$ such that $\cap \overline{\mathfrak{F}} = \emptyset$. Using Zorn's lemma we can easily prove that there exists a maximal centered system $\mathfrak{G}$ of members of $\mathfrak{U}^{\vee}$ which contains $\mathfrak{F}$. If $\mathfrak{F} = \{F_\alpha | \alpha \in A\}$, then for fixed $\alpha \in A$, there exists a finite subcollection $\{U_i | i=1,2,\ldots,n\}$ of $\mathfrak{U}$ such that $F_\alpha = \cup \{U_i | i=1,2,\ldots,n\} \in \mathfrak{F} \subset \mathfrak{G}$. By maximality of $\mathfrak{G}$, we can select an index i ($1 \leq i \leq n$) such that $U_i \in \mathfrak{G}$; let us denote this U_i by U_α. By assumption we have $\cap \{\overline{U}_\alpha | \alpha \in A\} \subset \cap \{\overline{F}_\alpha | \alpha \in A\} = \emptyset$; thus basiscompactness of X relative to $\mathfrak{U}$ yields the existence of a finite subcollection $\{U_{\alpha_1}, U_{\alpha_2}, \ldots, U_{\alpha_k}\}$ of $\{U_\alpha | \alpha \in A\}$ with empty intersection. Since $U_{\alpha_i} \in \mathfrak{G}$, this contradicts the fact that $\mathfrak{G}$ is a centered system.

2.1.5. Recall that an open set O of a topological space is called *regular open* provided that $\overline{O}^{o} = O$. A space is called *semiregular* if it has a base consisting of regular open sets.

PROPOSITION. Every semiregular basiscompact space is basiscompact relative to a base consisting of regular open sets.

PROOF. Let X be a semiregular space which is basiscompact relative to a base $\mathfrak{U}$ for its topology. Denote by $\mathfrak{U}'$ the collection $\{\overline{U}^{o} | U \in \mathfrak{U}\}$; by the semiregularity of X it follows that $\mathfrak{U}'$ is also a base for the topology. We will show that X is basiscompact relative to $\mathfrak{U}'$. Let $\{\overline{U}^{o} | U \in \mathfrak{U}_1\}$ be a centered system $(\mathfrak{U}_1 \subset \mathfrak{U})$. Then $\mathfrak{U}_1$ is also a centered system, since for each finite subcollection $\{U_1,\ldots,U_n\}$ of $\mathfrak{U}$, the assertion $U_1 \cap \ldots \cap U_n = \emptyset$ implies $\overline{U}_1^{o} \cap \ldots \cap \overline{U}_n^{o} = \emptyset$. Thus by assumption we have $\bigcap \{\overline{U} | U \in \mathfrak{U}_1\} \neq \emptyset$. Since $\overline{U} = \overline{\overline{U}^{o}}$, we also have $\bigcap \{\overline{\overline{U}^{o}} | U \in \mathfrak{U}_1\} \neq \emptyset$, proving that X is basiscompact relative to $\mathfrak{U}'$.

2.1.6. Recall that a mapping f from a space X onto a space Y is called *perfect* if it is continuous, closed (the images of closed sets are closed) and the inverse images of points are compact. f is called *irreducible* if $f(S) \neq Y$ for each proper closed subset S of X.

THEOREM. If f is a perfect irreducible map of a basiscompact space X onto a space Y, then Y is basiscompact.

Before proving this theorem we first mention a few properties of perfect and perfect irreducible mappings, which are known from the literature. For the sake of completeness we also give the proofs.

LEMMA 1. Let f be a perfect map of a space X onto a space Y and $\mathfrak{U}$ a base for the topology of X which is closed under finite unions. Then the collection $\{Y \setminus f(X \setminus U) | U \in \mathfrak{U}\}$ constitutes a base for the topology of Y.

PROOF. Let O be a neighborhood of a point p in Y. For each point q of $f^{-1}(p)$ let U_q be a basicneighborhood of q which is mapped into O by f. The compactness of $f^{-1}(p)$ yields the existence of a finite subcollection $\{U_{q1},\ldots,U_{qn}\}$ of $\{U_q | q \in f^{-1}(p)\}$ which covers $f^{-1}(p)$. By assumption $U = \bigcup \{U_{qi} | i=1,2,\ldots,n\} \in \mathfrak{U}$ and $Y \setminus f(X \setminus U)$ is an open set of Y satisfying $p \in Y \setminus f(X \setminus U) \subset O$.

LEMMA 2. Let X and Y be topological spaces and f a perfect map of X onto Y. Then there exists a closed subset S of X such that the restriction map $f|S$ is a perfect irreducible map of S onto Y.

PROOF. Let $\mathfrak{F} = \{F_\alpha | \alpha \in A\}$ be the family of all closed subsets of X with the property $f(F_\alpha) = Y$. Define a partial order $<$ on $\mathfrak{F}$ such that the inequality $F_\alpha < F_\beta$ holds iff $F_\beta \subset F_\alpha$. Let $\mathfrak{F}_1 = \{F_\alpha | \alpha \in A_1 \subset A\}$ be an arbitrary chain of $\mathfrak{F}$ and y an arbitrary point of Y. Then $\{F_\alpha \cap f^{-1}(y) | \alpha \in A_1\}$ is a centered system and compactness of $f^{-1}(y)$ yields $\cap \{F_\alpha | \alpha \in A_1\} \cap f^{-1}(y) \neq \emptyset$, i.e. $\cap \{F_\alpha | \alpha \in A_1\} \in \mathfrak{F}$. Thus $\mathfrak{F}_1$ has an upper bound in $\mathfrak{F}$. Using Zorn's lemma, we conclude that $\mathfrak{F}$ has a maximal element S. The restriction map $f|S$ is a perfect irreducible map of S onto Y.

LEMMA 3. Let f be a closed irreducible map of a space X onto a space Y. If O is an open set of X, then $\overline{f(O)} = \overline{Y \setminus f(X \setminus O)}$.

PROOF. It suffices to prove $\overline{f(O)} \subset \overline{Y \setminus f(X \setminus O)}$. It is evident that $\overline{f[(X \setminus O) \cup f^{-1}(Y \setminus f(X \setminus O))]} = Y$, and since f is an irreducible map, it follows that $(X \setminus O) \cup \overline{f^{-1}(Y \setminus f(X \setminus O))} = X$, i.e., $O \subset \overline{f^{-1}(Y \setminus f(X \setminus O))}$. Thus from the closedness of f, we conclude that $f(O) \subset \overline{Y \setminus f(X \setminus O))}$.

PROOF OF THE THEOREM.

Let X be a basiscompact space and f a perfect irreducible map of X onto Y. It follows from 2.1.4. that X is basiscompact relative to a base $\mathfrak{U}$ which is closed under finite unions. By lemma 1 the collection $F\mathfrak{U} = \{Y \setminus f(X \setminus U)) | U \in \mathfrak{U}\}$ is a base for the topology of Y. We shall prove that Y is basiscompact relative to $F\mathfrak{U}$.
Let $\mathfrak{F} = \{Y \setminus f(X \setminus U) | U \in \mathfrak{U}_1\}$ be a centered system of members of $F\mathfrak{U}$. Then it is easy to see that $\mathfrak{U}_1$ is a centered system of members of $\mathfrak{U}$. Indeed if there would exist $U_1, \ldots, U_n \in \mathfrak{U}_1$ with empty intersection, then $\{X \setminus U_1, \ldots, X \setminus U_n\}$ is a cover of X. Consequently

$\{f(X \setminus U_1),\dots,f(X \setminus U_n)\}$ is a cover of $f(X) = Y$ i.e. $\cap \{Y \setminus f(X \setminus U_i) | 1 \leq i \leq n\} = \emptyset$, which is impossible. Basiscompactness of X relative to $\mathfrak{U}$ yields the existence of a point p in $\cap \{\bar{U} | U \in \mathfrak{U}_1\}$. Hence $f(p) \in \cap \{f(\bar{U}) | U \in \mathfrak{U}_1\}$. However by the previous lemma we have $\overline{f(U)} = \overline{Y \setminus f(X \setminus U)}$ for each $U \in \mathfrak{U}_1$; thus $f(p) \in \cap \{\overline{Y \setminus f(X \setminus U)} | U \in \mathfrak{U}_1\} = \cap \bar{\mathfrak{J}}$. This completes the proof of the theorem.

REMARK. It is an open problem whether or not the above result remains valid for arbitrary perfect mappings (not necessarily irreducible). Note that every perfect image of a basiscompact metrizable space is basiscompact (this follows at once from 2.1.6., lemma 2 and the next theorem).

2.1.7. THEOREM. A metrizable space is basiscompact if and only if it is topologically complete.

PROOF. Necessity (compare with [11]). Let (M,ρ) be a basiscompact metric space. Let (M^*,ρ) denote the (metric) completion of (M,ρ). We will show that M is a G_δ-subset of M^*, which yields a proof of this part of the theorem by the ALEXANDROFF-HAUSDORFF theorem. Let $\mathfrak{U}$ be a base for the metric topology of M relative to which M is basiscompact. Define for each $i = 1,2,\dots,\mathfrak{U}_i = \{U \in \mathfrak{U} | \text{diam } U < \frac{1}{i}\}$. Observe that for each i, $\mathfrak{U}_i$ is an open base for M, thus $\mathfrak{U}_i$ is a cover of M. For each $U \in \mathfrak{U}$, let U^* be an open set of M^* such that $U^* \cap M = U$. Since M is dense in M^*, the diameters of U and U^* are equal. Define $O_i^* = \cup \{U^* | U \in \mathfrak{U}_i\}$; we shall prove that $M = \cap \{O_i^* | i=1,2,\dots\}$. Trivially $M \subset \cap \{O_i^* | i=1,2,\dots\}$. Let us suppose that there exists a point p in $\cap \{O_i^* | i=1,2,\dots\}$ which is not an element of M. For each i, select a member $U_i \in \mathfrak{U}_i$ with the property $p \in U_i^*$. The collection $\{U_i | i=1,2,\dots\}$ is a centered system of members of $\mathfrak{U}$; hence basiscompactness of M relative to $\mathfrak{U}$ yields $\cap \{\bar{U}_i^M | i=1,2,\dots\} \neq \emptyset$. Let us suppose that q is a point of $\cap \{\overline{U_i}^M | i=1,2,\ldots\}$. Clearly $p \neq q$ and because the diameters of the U_i^* tend to zero, there exists a natural number n such that $p \in U_n^*$ and the closure in M^* of U_n^* is disjoint from q. It follows that $q \notin \cap \{\overline{U_i^*}^{M^*} | i=1,2,\ldots\} = \cap \{\overline{U_i}^M | i=1,2,\ldots\}$ (since M is dense in M^*). This gives the desired contradiction.

Sufficiency. We first note that a zerodimensional completely metrizable space M is basiscompact. Indeed, by virtue of the zerodimensionality of M, there exists for each i a cover $\mathfrak{U}_i$ of M consisting of pairwise disjoint clopen sets each of diameter $< \frac{1}{i}$ (see [26] page 22). Thus M is basiscompact relative to $\cup \{\mathfrak{U}_i | i=1,2,\ldots\}$. If M is an arbitrary (not necessary zerodimensional) completely metrizable space, then a theorem of MORITA (see [27] or [28] for a simpler proof) states that M is the image of a zerodimensional completely metrizable space under a perfect mapping f. By virtue of lemma 2 we may suppose that f is an irreducible mapping. Hence, M being a perfect irreducible image of a basiscompact space is basiscompact by theorem 2.1.6.

2.1.8. An obvious modification of the proof of 2.1.7. yields the following more general result.

THEOREM. A regular space is a completely metrizable space if and only if it is basiscompact relative to a σ-locally finite base for its topology.

2.1.9. THEOREM. Each basiscompact regular space is a Baire space.

PROOF. Let $\{A_i | i=1,2,\ldots\}$ be a countable collection of nowhere dense closed subsets of a regular space X which is basiscompact relative to a base $\mathfrak{U}$ for its topology. Let O be a non empty open set of X. By induction we construct for each $k = 1,2,\ldots$ non empty elements U_k of $\mathfrak{U}$ with the properties $\overline{U}_i \subset U_{i-1}$ and $U_i \cap A_i = \emptyset$ for $i=1,2,\ldots,k$. For $k = 1$, let U_1 be some non empty element of $\mathfrak{U}_1$ whose closure is contained in O and which is disjoint from A_1. If U_j for

$1 < j < k$ is already defined with the desired properties, then let p be some point of U_{k-1} which is not in A_k and define U_k as being an element of $\mathfrak{U}$ which satisfies $p \in U_k \subset \overline{U}_k \subset U_{k-1}$, $U_k \cap A_k = \emptyset$. The collection $\{U_k | k=1,2,\ldots\}$ thus defined is a centered system of members of $\mathfrak{U}$. Thus, by basiscompactness of X relative to $\mathfrak{U}$, it follows that $D = \cap\{\overline{U}_k | k=1,2,\ldots\} = \cap\{U_k | k=1,2,\ldots\} \neq \emptyset$. The construction of the U_k's insures that $D \cap \cup \{A_i | i=1,2,\ldots\} = \emptyset$ and $D \subset O$. Thus $X \setminus \cup \{A_i | i=1,2,\ldots\}$ is a dense subset of X. This completes the proof of the theorem.

2. m-ULTRACOMPACTNESS

In this section we define the concept of m-ultracompactness for any infinite cardinal number m. m-ultracompactness resembles, to some extent, the property k-compactness introduced by HERRLICH [15], and for $m = \aleph_1$, the property almost-realcompactness introduced by FROLIK [9].

m-ultracompactness is closed-hereditary and productive, it is possessed by all compact spaces, and $\aleph_1$-ultracompactness coincides with realcompactness in countably paracompact normal spaces. Furthermore, m-ultracompactness is a fitting property, i.e., if f is a perfect map of a space X onto a space Y, then both or neither of X and Y must be m-ultracompact.

2.2.1. A family of subsets of a topological space X has the *m-intersection property* (m being an infinite cardinal number) provided that every subcollection of cardinal $< m$ has non empty intersection. If $\mathfrak{S}$ is a closed subbase for a space X, then X is called *m-ultracompact relative to* $\mathfrak{S}$ iff each ultrafilter $\mathfrak{F}$ in X, for which $\mathfrak{F} \cap \mathfrak{S}$ satisfies the m-intersection property, is convergent. A space

X is called *m-ultracompact* if there exists a closed subbase $\mathfrak{S}$ for its topology such that X is m-ultracompact relative to $\mathfrak{S}$.

2.2.2. It is obvious that compactness is equivalent with $\aleph_0$-ultracompactness. There also exist relationships between $\aleph_1$-ultracompactness and realcompactness. Indeed, a completely regular space is realcompact iff it is $\aleph_1$-ultracompact relative to the (sub)base consisting of all zerosets ([10, page 153]). In chapter III we shall generalize this result and obtain separation conditions for a subbase $\mathfrak{S}$ such that $\aleph_1$-ultracompactness relative to $\mathfrak{S}$ implies realcompactness and complete regularity (see theorem 3.1.8).

2.2.3. If a space X is m-ultracompact relative to some closed subbase $\mathfrak{S}$, then it is easy to prove that each maximal centered family of members of $\mathfrak{S}$ with the m-intersection property has non empty intersection. In the next chapter we prove (for $m = \aleph_1$) that under certain conditions on $\mathfrak{S}$ the latter statement also implies the former (lemma 3.1.4.). Although we do not know whether or not this is true for arbitrary subbases we still have the following result.

PROPOSITION. Let X be a space and $\mathfrak{S}$ a closed subbase for X with the property that each subcollection of $\mathfrak{S}$ with the m-intersection property has non empty intersection. Then X is m-ultracompact relative to $\mathfrak{S}$.

PROOF. Let $\mathfrak{F}$ be an ultrafilter in X such that $\mathfrak{F} \cap \mathfrak{S}$ satisfies the m-intersection property. Let us suppose that, on the contrary, $\mathfrak{F}$ has no limit point in X. Since the collection $\{X \setminus S \mid S \in \mathfrak{S}\}$ is a subbase for the open sets of X, there exists for each $p \in X$ a subbasicneighborhood $X \setminus S_p$ of p which is not a member of $\mathfrak{F}$. It follows that $\{X \setminus S_p \mid p \in X\}$ is a cover of X and consequently $\cap \{S_p \mid p \in X\} = \emptyset$. By assumption there exists a subcollection $\{S_{p_\alpha} \mid \alpha \in A\}$ of $\{S_p \mid p \in X\}$ of cardinality $< m$ with empty intersection. This contradicts that $\mathfrak{F} \cap \mathfrak{S}$ satisfies the m-intersection property.

2.2.4. We shall say that an ultrafilter $\mathfrak{F}$ in a space X is an m-*ultrafilter* (m being an infinite cardinal number) provided that the collection of closed members of $\mathfrak{F}$ satisfies the m-intersection property. Then it is obvious that a space is m-ultracompact if and only if each m-ultrafilter is convergent.

LEMMA. Let $\mathfrak{F}$ be an m-ultrafilter in a space X and $f: X \to Y$ a continuous mapping. The collection $\mathfrak{G} = \{f(F) | F \in \mathfrak{F}\}$ constitutes a base for an m-ultrafilter in Y.

PROOF. It is obvious that $\mathfrak{G}$ is a base for an ultrafilter $\mathfrak{G}'$ in X. Let $\{S_\alpha | \alpha \in A\}$ be a family of closed sets of $\mathfrak{G}'$ with cardinal $< m$. Clearly every S_α intersects every $f(F)$ $(F \in \mathfrak{F})$. Consequently, every $f^{-1}(S_\alpha)$ is a non empty closed subset of X which meets every member of $\mathfrak{F}$. Since $\mathfrak{F}$ is an m-ultrafilter, $\{f^{-1}(S_\alpha) | \alpha \in A\}$ is a subcollection of $\mathfrak{F}$ and $\cap \{f^{-1}(S_\alpha) | \alpha \in A\} \neq \emptyset$. It follows that $\{S_\alpha | \alpha \in A\}$ has non empty intersection.

2.2.5. THEOREM. For every cardinal m the property m-ultracompactness is closed-hereditary and productive.

PROOF. Let $\{X_\alpha | \alpha \in A\}$ be a collection of m-ultracompact spaces and let $X = \Pi\{X_\alpha | \alpha \in A\}$. For an m-ultrafilter $\mathfrak{F}$ in X, let $\mathfrak{F}_\alpha =$ $= \{\pi_\alpha F | F \in \mathfrak{F}\}$ for $\alpha \in A$. By the previous lemma, each $\mathfrak{F}_\alpha$ is a base for an m-ultrafilter in X_α which is convergent to a point p_α in X_α. The point p of X whose α'th coordinate is p_α is a limit point of $\mathfrak{F}$; hence $\mathfrak{F}$ is a convergent filter.

Now let X be an m-ultracompact space and Y a closed subspace of X. We will show that Y is m-ultracompact. Suppose that $\mathfrak{F}$ is an m-ultrafilter in Y. The preceding lemma shows that $\mathfrak{F}$ is a base for an m-ultrafilter $\mathfrak{F}'$ in X which is convergent, to some $p \in X$. Clearly $p \in \cap \{\overline{F} | F \in \mathfrak{F}'\} \subset \cap \{\overline{F}^Y | F \in \mathfrak{F}\}$. Hence $\mathfrak{F}$ is a convergent filter in Y. This completes the proof of the theorem.

2.2.6. THEOREM. Every space Y which is the perfect image of some m-ultracompact space X under a mapping f is m-ultracompact. Moreover, m-ultracompactness is a fitting property.

PROOF. Let $\mathfrak{F}$ be an arbitrary m-ultrafilter in Y and $\mathfrak{G}$ an ultrafilter in X which contains the family $f^{-1}(\mathfrak{F}) = \{f^{-1}(F) \mid F \in \mathfrak{F}\}$. We shall first prove that $\mathfrak{G}$ is an m-ultrafilter in X. Let us suppose that there exists a family $\mathfrak{S}$ of closed members of $\mathfrak{G}$ of cardinal $< m$ with empty intersection. Without loss of generality we may suppose that $\mathfrak{S}$ is closed under finite intersections. The members of $f(\mathfrak{S}) = \{f(S) \mid S \in \mathfrak{S}\}$ are closed subsets of Y and they intersect each member of $\mathfrak{F}$. Consequently, $f(\mathfrak{S}) \subset \mathfrak{F}$ and we are able to choose $p \in \bigcap f(\mathfrak{S})$ since $\mathfrak{F}$ is an m-ultrafilter in Y. Now $\{f^{-1}(p) \cap S \mid S \in \mathfrak{S}\}$ is a centered system in X and so compactness of $f^{-1}(p)$ yields $\bigcap \{f^{-1}(p) \cap S \mid S \in \mathfrak{S}\} \neq \emptyset$. Hence $\bigcap \mathfrak{S} \neq \emptyset$, which contradicts our assumption. The space X being m-ultracompact implies $\bigcap \overline{\mathfrak{G}}^X \neq \emptyset$, and consequently, $\bigcap \overline{\mathfrak{F}}^Y \neq \emptyset$. The second statement follows from 1.2.5.

2.2.7. THEOREM. (compare with [15]). For each cardinal number $\aleph_\alpha$ there exists a completely regular space T_α which is $\aleph_\alpha$-ultracompact but not $\aleph_\beta$-ultracompact for $\beta < \alpha$.

PROOF. If $\aleph_\alpha$ is not a limit cardinal then the collection $T_\alpha = \{\xi \mid \xi$ an ordinal $< \omega_\alpha\}$, endowed with the usual order topology, is a space which is $\aleph_\alpha$-ultracompact but not $\aleph_\beta$-ultracompact for $\beta < \alpha$. Indeed, it is wellknown that there exists exactly one free ultrafilter $\mathfrak{F}$ in T_α. $\mathfrak{F}$ is an $\aleph_{\alpha-1}$-ultrafilter but not an $\aleph_\alpha$-ultrafilter.
If $\aleph_\alpha$ is a limit cardinal number, then let $\aleph_\alpha = \sup \{\aleph_\gamma \mid \gamma \in \Gamma\}$ where each $\aleph_\gamma$ is a non limit cardinal smaller than $\aleph_\alpha$. Define T_γ for $\gamma \in \Gamma$ as above, and let $T_\alpha = \Pi \{T_\gamma \mid \gamma \in \Gamma\}$. It is obvious that T_α is $\aleph_\alpha$-ultracompact, for it is the product of $\aleph_\alpha$-ultracompact spaces. T_α is not $\aleph_\beta$-ultracompact for $\beta < \alpha$. Indeed, if on the contrary there exists $\beta < \alpha$ such that T_α is $\aleph_\beta$-ultracompact, then let $\gamma \in \Gamma$ satisfy $\beta < \gamma < \alpha$. Since T_γ is a closed subspace of T_α it follows that T_γ is $\aleph_\beta$-ultracompact, which is impossible. The theorem now follows.

2.2.8. THEOREM. In a countably paracompact normal space X, the following conditions are equivalent

1. X is realcompact
2. X is $\aleph_1$-ultracompact
3. For every maximal centered system $\mathfrak{D}$ of open sets for which $\overline{\mathfrak{D}}$ satisfies the countable intersection property, the intersection $\cap\overline{\mathfrak{D}}$ is non empty (i.e., X is almost-realcompact in the sense of [9]).

PROOF. The pattern of proof is 1 $\Longrightarrow$ 2 $\Longrightarrow$ 3 $\Longrightarrow$ 1.

1 $\Longrightarrow$ 2. Recall (cf. [10] page 153) that a space is realcompact iff each ultrafilter, for which the collection of zerosets satisfies the countable intersection property, is convergent.

2 $\Longrightarrow$ 3. Let $\mathfrak{D}$ be a maximal centered family of open sets. By Zorn's lemma there exists an ultrafilter $\mathfrak{F}$ which contains $\mathfrak{D}$ as a subcollection.We shall prove that $\mathfrak{F}$ is an $\aleph_1$-ultrafilter. Then it will follow that $\mathfrak{F}$ is convergent, and in particular, $\cap\overline{\mathfrak{D}} \neq \emptyset$. Let us suppose, on the contrary, that there exists a countable collection $\{S_i \mid i=1,2,\ldots\}$ of closed members of $\mathfrak{F}$ with empty intersection. The family $\{X \setminus S_i \mid i=1,2,\ldots\}$ is obviously a countable cover of X which, by virtue of the countable paracompactness of X (see [27]) has a countable closed refinement $\{T_j \mid j=1,2,\ldots\}$.

Since $\overline{\mathfrak{D}}$ satisfies the countable intersection property, there exists a natural number k such that T_k intersects each member of $\overline{\mathfrak{D}}$. Select a natural number l such that $T_k \subset X \setminus S_l$ or, equivalently, $T_k \cap S_l = \emptyset$, and let O be an open neighborhood of S_l whose closure is disjoint from T_k (use the normality of X). By maximality of $\mathfrak{D}$, we have $O \in \mathfrak{D}$ and consequently, $\overline{O}$ is a member of $\overline{\mathfrak{D}}$ which does not intersect T_k. This gives the desired contradiction.

3 $\Longrightarrow$ 1. This was already proved by FROLIK [9].

2.2.9. THEOREM. Let f be a perfect map of a space X onto a space Y and suppose that X is countably paracompact and normal. Then Y is realcompact if and only if X is realcompact.

PROOF. A well known result states that Y is countably paracompact and normal. So the theorem follows from 2.2.6. and 2.2.8.

2.2.10. NOTES. 2.2.9. was first proved by FROLIK [9] (he stated 2.2.9. for normal spaces, but in the proof he essentially used countable paracompactness).

It is an open problem whether or not every closed continuous image of a realcompact space is realcompact, or even whether the condition of countable paracompactness in 2.2.9. can be dropped. In this context we note a recent result of ISIWATA [22] which states that a closed continuous image of a locally compact countably paracompact normal realcompact space is realcompact.

It is also an open problem whether or not the equivalence in 2.2.8. remains satisfied if we drop the condition of countable paracompactness.

CHAPTER III

A GENERAL REALCOMPACTIFICATION METHOD

1. THE REALCOMPACTIFICATION $\upsilon(\mathfrak{S})X$

3.1.0. Let X be a T_1-space. For closed subbases of X we consider two separation conditions, namely the conditions of subbase-regularity and subbase-normality (for a precise definition see 3.1.1. of this thesis). The definitions are such that in case X is completely regular, then the family of zerosets of X is a (sub)base which satisfies the conditions of subbase-regularity and subbase-normality. In general, however, our subbases will not be closed under the set theoretical operations of taking finite unions and finite intersections.

In [1] AARTS has proved that if $\mathfrak{S}$ is a subbase for the closed sets of a space X, which satisfies the conditions of subbase-regularity and subbase-normality, then there exists a Hausdorff compactification $\beta(\mathfrak{S})X$ of X such that 1) the closures in $\beta(\mathfrak{S})X$ of the members of $\mathfrak{S}$ form a closed subbase for $\beta(\mathfrak{S})X$, 2) every two disjoint members of $\mathfrak{S}$ have disjoint closures in $\beta(\mathfrak{S})X$. In particular, if we take for $\mathfrak{S}$ the family of all zerosets, then the construction insures that $\beta(\mathfrak{S})X$ coincides with the Čech-Stone compactification of X.

In this section an analogous result is obtained for the realcompact case. If $\mathfrak{S}$ is a closed subbase for a space X which satisfies the conditions of subbase-regularity and subbase-normality, and moreover, satisfies a certain countability condition, then there exists a (unique) completely regular realcompactification $\upsilon(\mathfrak{S})X$ of X with the following properties: 1) The closures in $\upsilon(\mathfrak{S})X$ of the members of $\mathfrak{S}$ form a closed subbase for $\upsilon(\mathfrak{S})X$; each maximal centered family of this collection with the countable intersection property has non empty intersection, 2) If a countable family of members of $\mathfrak{S}$ has empty intersection in X, then their closures in $\upsilon(\mathfrak{S})X$ have empty intersection in $\upsilon(\mathfrak{S})X$.

The basic construction of $\upsilon(\mathfrak{S})X$ is as follows: Let $\beta(\mathfrak{S})X$ be the

compactification of X described above. For each countable cover $\mathfrak{U}$ of X by members of $\mathfrak{S}$, consider the subspace of $\beta(\mathfrak{S})X$ which is the union of the closures in $\beta(\mathfrak{S})X$ of the members of $\mathfrak{U}$.
The intersection of all these subspaces, when $\mathfrak{U}$ is running through all the countable covers of X by members of $\mathfrak{S}$, yields our realcompactification $\upsilon(\mathfrak{S})x$.

As in the previous result we have $\upsilon(\mathfrak{S})X = X$ if and only if each maximal centered family of members of $\mathfrak{S}$ with the countable intersection property has non empty intersection, this yields an intrinsic characterization of realcompactness which seems to be new.

3.1.1. Two subsets A and B of a topological space X are said to be *screened* by a finite family $\mathfrak{F}$ of subsets of X if $\mathfrak{F}$ covers X and each element of $\mathfrak{F}$ meets at most one of A and B.

A subbase $\mathfrak{S}$ for the closed sets of a space X satisfies the *condition of subbase-regularity* if for each $S \in \mathfrak{S}$ and $x \notin S$, there exist subsets $S_1, \ldots, S_n$ of X such that $\bigcup \{S_i \mid i=1,2,\ldots,n\} = S$ and each pair (x, S_i) is screened by a finite subcollection of $\mathfrak{S}$. $\mathfrak{S}$ satisfies the *condition of subbase-normality* if each two disjoint elements of $\mathfrak{S}$ are screened by a finite subcollection of $\mathfrak{S}$.

If no confusion is possible, then, instead of saying that a subbase $\mathfrak{S}$ satisfies the condition of subbase-regularity, we simply will say that $\mathfrak{S}$ satisfies the regularity condition. The expression "condition of subbase-normality" will be abbreviated in a similar way. Note, that the condition of subbase-regularity (subbase-normality) is weaker than the condition of base-regularity introduced in Chapter II, section 2.

EXAMPLES. 1. The family of all closed sets of a regular space is a closed (sub)base which satisfies the regularity condition.
2. The family of all closed sets of a normal space is a closed (sub) base which satisfies the regularity and normality conditions (cf. [10] page 17).

3. Let X be a set and C be a family of mappings of X into R with the following properties:

a. C separates points

b. C contains all constant mappings

c. $f \in C \Longrightarrow |f| \in C$

d. $f,g \in C \Longrightarrow \lambda f + \mu g \in C$ $(\lambda,\mu \in R)$

e. $f \in C$, $f(x) \neq 0$ for all $x \in X \Longrightarrow \frac{1}{f} \in C$.

Then the collection $\mathfrak{S} = \{\{x \in X \mid f(x) = 0\} \mid f \in C\}$ constitutes a subbase for a topology on X which satisfies the regularity and normality conditions. In particular, it follows that the family of all zero-sets of a completely regular space is a subbase which satisfies the regularity and normality conditions.

3.1.2. The following theorem (AARTS and DE GROOT [1,13]) states that the existence of a closed subbase which satisfies the regularity and normality conditions implies complete regularity.

THEOREM. Let $\mathfrak{S}$ be a closed subbase for a space X which satisfies the regularity and normality conditions. Then there exists a Hausdorff compactification $\beta(\mathfrak{S})X$ of X with the following properties:

1. The closures in $\beta(\mathfrak{S})X$ of the members of $\mathfrak{S}$ form a closed subbase for $\beta(\mathfrak{S})X$, which satisfies the regularity and normality conditions.

2. Every two disjoint members of $\mathfrak{S}$ have disjoint closures in $\beta(\mathfrak{S})X$.

SKETCH OF THE PROOF [1)]. We consider the collection M of all maximal centered families of members of $\mathfrak{S}$; if $\mu \in M$ then we define $\bar{\mu}$ as the collection of members of $\mathfrak{S}$ which intersect each member of μ. Such an obtained collection $\bar{\mu}$ is called a linked system. If $\mathfrak{S}$ is not closed under finite intersections, then in general $\bar{\mu}$ is not a centered system. However, it easily follows from the normality condition of $\mathfrak{S}$ that every two members of $\bar{\mu}$ have non empty intersection.

---

1) This proof is due to J. DE GROOT [13]. Another way of proving this theorem was earlier pointed out by J.M. AARTS [1].

Now, let $\beta(\mathfrak{S})X = \{\overline{\mu} \mid \mu \in M\}$ and for each $S \in \mathfrak{S}$, $S^* = \{\overline{\mu} \mid S \in \overline{\mu}\}$. The collection $\{S^* \mid S \in \mathfrak{S}\}$ is a subbase for a topology on $\beta(\mathfrak{S})X$, and if we identify each point $x \in X$ with the linked system $\{S \in \mathfrak{S} \mid x \in S\}$, then X becomes a dense subspace of $\beta(\mathfrak{S})X$. For the star operator, we can easily prove the following identities: $S \subset S^*$, $S^* \cap T^* = \emptyset$ iff $S \cap T = \emptyset$; $S_1^* \cup \ldots \cup S_n^* = \beta(\mathfrak{S})X$ iff $S_1 \cup \ldots \cup S_n = X$. Thus, by the regularity and normality conditions of $\mathfrak{S}$ and the fact that for each $S \in \mathfrak{S}$ we have $S \subset \overline{S}^{\beta(\mathfrak{S})X} \subset S^*$ [1), it easily follows that the closures in $\beta(\mathfrak{S})X$ of the members of $\mathfrak{S}$ form a closed subbase of $\beta(\mathfrak{S})X$ which satisfies the regularity and normality conditions. One can prove that each (maximal) centered system of members of $\mathfrak{S}^*$ has non empty intersection in $\beta(\mathfrak{S})X$. Thus $\beta(\mathfrak{S})X$ is a Hausdorff compactification of X with the desired properties. The theorem now follows.

3.1.3. A subbase $\mathfrak{S}$ for the closed sets of a space X satisfies the *countability condition* iff each countable cover of X by members of $\{X \setminus S \mid S \in \mathfrak{S}\}$ has a countable refinement by members of $\mathfrak{S}$.

EXAMPLE 1. In a countably paracompact normal space, the family of all closed sets is a closed (sub)base which satisfies the countability condition. In a completely regular space, the family of all zerosets is a closed (sub)base which satisfies the countability condition.

PROOF. For the first statement, note that a space is countably paracompact iff each countable open cover has a countable closed refinement. For the second statement, note that every cozeroset of a space is a countable union of zerosets.

EXAMPLE 2. The subbase defined in 3.1.1. Example 3 satisfies the countability condition.

---

1) As was pointed out by J. de Groot, in general it is not true that S^* is equal to the closure in $\beta(\mathfrak{S})X$ of S.

3.1.4. Recall that if $\mathfrak{S}$ is a family of subsets of a topological space X, then a centered system $\mathfrak{F}$ of members of $\mathfrak{S}$ is *prime* iff each finite cover of X by members of $\mathfrak{S}$ contains a member of $\mathfrak{F}$.

LEMMA. Let $\mathfrak{S}$ be a closed subbase for a space X which satisfies the regularity, normality and countability conditions. Then the following conditions are equivalent:

(i) Every maximal centered system of members of $\mathfrak{S}$ with c.i.p. (countable intersection property) has non empty intersection.

(ii) Every prime centered system of members of $\mathfrak{S}$ with c.i.p. has non empty intersection.

(iii) Every ultrafilter $\mathfrak{F}$ for which $\mathfrak{F} \cap \mathfrak{S}$ has c.i.p. is convergent, i.e., X is $\aleph_1$-ultracompact relative to $\mathfrak{S}$.

PROOF. (i) $\Longrightarrow$ (ii). Let $\mathfrak{F}$ be a prime centered system of members of $\mathfrak{S}$ with the countable intersection property. $\mathfrak{F}$ is contained in some maximal centered system $\mathfrak{G}$ of members of $\mathfrak{S}$; hence, it suffices to show that $\mathfrak{G}$ has the countable intersection property.
Suppose, on the contrary, that there exists a countable subcollection $\{G_i \mid i=1,2,\dots\}$ of $\mathfrak{G}$ with empty intersection. Since $\mathfrak{S}$ satisfies the countability condition, the countable cover $\{X \setminus G_i \mid i=1,2,\dots\}$ has a countable refinement $\{S_n \mid n=1,2,\dots\}$ consisting of members of $\mathfrak{S}$. For each n = 1, 2, ... select an index i_n such that $S_n \subset X \setminus G_{i_n}$ and a finite cover $\mathfrak{E}_n$ of X by members of $\mathfrak{S}$ which screens S_n and G_{i_n}. Since $\mathfrak{F}$ is prime, for n = 1, 2, ..., there exists $E_n \in \mathfrak{E}_n$ such that $E_n \in \mathfrak{F}$. Obviously, $E_n \cap G_{i_n} \neq \emptyset$ since $\mathfrak{G}$ is a centered system, and so $E_n \cap S_n = \emptyset$. It follows that $\cap \{E_n \mid n=1,2,\dots\} = \emptyset$. This contradicts the fact that $\mathfrak{F}$ has the countable intersection property.

(ii) $\Longrightarrow$ (iii). Let $\mathfrak{F}$ be an ultrafilter in X for which $\mathfrak{F} \cap \mathfrak{S}$ has c.i.p. Obviously, $\mathfrak{F} \cap \mathfrak{S}$ is a prime centered system that has c.i.p., and by hypothesis $\cap (\mathfrak{F} \cap \mathfrak{S}) \neq \emptyset$. Let us suppose that $p \in \cap (\mathfrak{F} \cap \mathfrak{S})$; it is enough to show that $\mathfrak{F}$ is convergent to p. Suppose, on the contrary, that there exists a neighborhood U of p which is not a member of $\mathfrak{F}$. Since $\{X \setminus S \mid S \in \mathfrak{S}\}$ is a subbase for the open sets of

X, there exists a finite collection $S_1, \ldots, S_n \in \mathfrak{S}$ such that $p \in V = \cap \{X \setminus S_i \mid i=1,2,\ldots,n\} \subset U$. Clearly, $V \notin \mathfrak{F}$ and since $\mathfrak{F}$ is closed under finite intersections, there exists i $(1 \leq i \leq n)$ such that $X \setminus S_i \notin \mathfrak{F}$. It follows that S_i is a member of $\mathfrak{F} \cap \mathfrak{S}$ which does not contain p. This contradicts the fact that $p \in \cap(\mathfrak{F} \cap \mathfrak{S})$

(iii) $\Longrightarrow$ (i). Let $\mathfrak{F}$ be a maximal centered system of members of $\mathfrak{S}$ with c.i.p.; if $\mathfrak{G}$ is some ultrafilter which contains the family $\mathfrak{F}$, then by maximality of $\mathfrak{F}$ it follows that $\mathfrak{G} \cap \mathfrak{S} = \mathfrak{F}$. Consequently $\mathfrak{G} \cap \mathfrak{S}$ has the countable intersection property. Thus $\cap \mathfrak{F} \neq \emptyset$, since $\mathfrak{G}$ is convergent.

REMARK. If $\mathfrak{S}$ is a closed subbase for a space X which satisfies the regularity condition, and if $\mathfrak{F}$ is a prime (maximal) centered system of members of $\mathfrak{S}$, then it is always true that $\cap \mathfrak{F}$ consists of at most one point. Indeed, if $p \in \cap \mathfrak{F}$ and if q is a point of X which is different from p, then there exists $S \subset X$ such that $p \in S$, $q \notin S$ and a finite cover $\{S_1, \ldots, S_n\}$ of X by members of $\mathfrak{S}$ which screens S and q. Since $\mathfrak{F}$ is prime, there exists i $(1 \leq i \leq n)$ such that $S_i \in \mathfrak{F}$. Obviously $p \in S_i$ and $q \notin S_i$. Thus S_i is a member of $\mathfrak{F}$ which does not contain q, i.e., $q \notin \cap \mathfrak{F}$.

3.1.5. Recall that a topological space is called *realcompact* provided that every maximal centered family of zerosets with the countable intersection property has non empty intersection. A *realcompactification* of a space X is a realcompact space which contains X as a dense subspace.

A well known theorem (of Hewitt and Shirota) states that the realcompact completely regular spaces are precisely those spaces which are homeomorphic with a closed subspace of a product of real lines. In particular, every metrizable space of non measurable cardinal is realcompact (see [10]).

It is well-known that every completely regular space X possesses a realcompactification υX (the so called *Hewitt realcompactification* of X) with the following properties: 1) $\{\overline{Z}^{\upsilon X} | Z \text{ is zeroset of } X\}$ is a base for the closed sets of υX, 2) if a countable family of zerosets of X has empty intersection in X, then their closures in υX have empty intersection in υX. The following theorem generalizes this result:

3.1.6. THEOREM. Let X be a T_1-space and $\mathfrak{S}$ a closed subbase for X which satisfies the regularity, normality and countability conditions. Then there exists a completely regular realcompactification $\upsilon(\mathfrak{S})X$ of X with the following properties:

1. The closures in $\upsilon(\mathfrak{S})X$ of the members of $\mathfrak{S}$ form a closed subbase for $\upsilon(\mathfrak{S})X$ which satisfies the regularity, normality and countability conditions. Each maximal centered system of members of this collection with c.i.p. has non empty intersection in $\upsilon(\mathfrak{S})X$.

2. If $\{S_i | i=1,2,\ldots\}$ is a countable subcollection of $\mathfrak{S}$ with empty intersection, then their closures in $\upsilon(\mathfrak{S})X$ have empty intersection in $\upsilon(\mathfrak{S})X$.

PROOF. Let $\beta(\mathfrak{S})X = Z$ be the Hausdorff compactification of X described in 3.1.2. Denote by $\delta = \{\mathfrak{U}\}$ the family of all countable covers of X by members of $\mathfrak{S}$. We will show that $Y = \cap \{\cup \overline{\mathfrak{U}}^Z | \mathfrak{U} \in \delta\}$ is a realcompactification of X with the desired properties, which we then denote by $\upsilon(\mathfrak{S})X$. It is obvious that Y is a realcompactification of X, since it is the intersection of σ-compact subspaces of Z (note that by virtue of 1.1.2. the property realcompactness is invariant for the taking of arbitrary intersections).
From the fact that $\overline{\mathfrak{S}}^Z$ is a closed subbase for Z (theorem 3.1.2.), it easily follows that $\overline{\mathfrak{S}}^Z \cap Y$ is a closed subbase for Y. From 3.1.2. we also easily deduce that $\overline{\mathfrak{S}}^Y$ satisfies the regularity and normality conditions. For the normality condition, note that if $\overline{S}^Y$ and $\overline{T}^Y$ are two disjoint members of $\overline{\mathfrak{S}}^Y$, then $\overline{S}^Z$ and $\overline{T}^Z$ are disjoint members of $\overline{\mathfrak{S}}^Z$. Thus a screening of $(\overline{S}^Z, \overline{T}^Z)$ by members of $\overline{\mathfrak{S}}^Z$ induces a screening of $(\overline{S}^Y, \overline{T}^Y)$ by members of $\overline{\mathfrak{S}}^Y$.

Let us verify that $\overline{\mathfrak{S}}^Y$ also satisfies the countability condition. Let $\{Y \setminus \overline{S}^Y | S \in \mathfrak{S}^1\}$ be a countable cover of Y by members of $\{Y \setminus \overline{S}^Y | S \in \mathfrak{S}\}$. Obviously, $\{X \setminus S | S \in \mathfrak{S}^1\}$ is a countable cover of

X and since $\mathfrak{S}$ satisfies the countability condition, it has a countable closed refinement $\mathfrak{T}$ consisting of members of $\mathfrak{S}$. The special definition of the subspace Y of Z immediately yields that $\overline{\mathfrak{T}}^Y$ is a countable cover of Y by members of $\overline{\mathfrak{S}}^Y$ and $\overline{\mathfrak{T}}^Y$ is a refinement of $\{Y \setminus \overline{S}^Y | S \in \mathfrak{S}^1\}$. For, if $\overline{T}^Y \in \overline{\mathfrak{T}}^Y$ for some $T \in \mathfrak{T}$, then there exists $S \in \mathfrak{S}^1$ such that $T \subset X \setminus S$, and so by 3.1.2.-2 $\overline{T}^Y \subset Y \setminus \overline{S}^Y$.

Next, we show that every maximal centered family of members of $\overline{\mathfrak{S}}^Y$ possessing c.i.p. has non empty intersection in Y. Let $\mathfrak{S}_1$ be a subcollection of $\mathfrak{S}$ such that $\overline{\mathfrak{S}}_1^Y$ is a maximal centered family of members of $\overline{\mathfrak{S}}^Y$ with the countable intersection property. By compactness of Z, there exists a point p in Z which is in the intersection of $\overline{\mathfrak{S}}_1^Z$. It is enough to show that $p \in Y$, whence it follows that $p \in \cap \overline{\mathfrak{S}}_1^Y$. For each countable cover $\mathfrak{U}$ of X by members of $\mathfrak{S}$, the collection $\overline{\mathfrak{U}}^Y$ is a countable cover of Y by members of $\overline{\mathfrak{S}}^Y$. Thus by maximality of $\overline{\mathfrak{S}}_1^Y$, each $\mathfrak{U}$ contains a member S such that $\overline{S}^Y \in \overline{\mathfrak{S}}_1^Y$, which implies that $p \in \overline{S}^Z$. Thus $p \in \cap \{\cup \overline{\mathfrak{U}}^Z | \mathfrak{U} \in \delta\}$, i.e., $p \in Y$.

PROOF OF 2. Let $\mathfrak{S}^1$ be a countable subcollection of $\mathfrak{S}$ with empty intersection. Then $\{X \setminus S | S \in \mathfrak{S}^1\}$ is a cover of X which has a countable refinement $\mathfrak{T}$ by members of $\mathfrak{S}$. The construction of Y immediately yields that $\overline{\mathfrak{T}}^Y$ is a cover of Y. Thus the intersection $\cap \{Y \setminus \overline{T}^Y | T \in \mathfrak{T}\}$ is empty. For each $T \in \mathfrak{T}$ there exists $S \in \mathfrak{S}^1$ such that $T \subset X \setminus S$ which implies $S \subset X \setminus T$ and also $\overline{S}^Y \subset Y \setminus \overline{T}^Y$, and so we conclude that the closures in Y of the members of $\mathfrak{S}^1$ have empty intersection in Y. This completes the proof of the theorem.

3.1.7. REMARKS. 1. If $\mathfrak{S}$ is a subbase which is closed under finite (countable) intersections then a different construction of $\upsilon(\mathfrak{S})X$ is possible. (This is the case when $\mathfrak{S}$ is the family of all zero-sets of a completely regular space.)

We consider the collection of all maximal centered systems of members of $\mathfrak{S}$ with the countable intersection property. Those centered systems which have empty intersection serve as new points and are

added to the space X. By choosing a suitable topology for the enlarged space, an extension X^* is obtained, from which we easily prove that it satisfies the conditions 1. and 2. of the previous theorem.
The results in the next section yield a method to prove that X^* is homeomorphic with $\upsilon(\mathfrak{S})X$; hence X^* is realcompact. (A direct proof of the realcompactness of X^* seems difficult).

The above method of extension of a space X to a space X^* was carried out by ALO and SHAPIRO [2]. However, they did not presuppose any separation condition on $\mathfrak{S}$ and so their construction did not yield a realcompactification method.

2. If $\mathfrak{S}$ is closed under countable intersections, then a slightly stronger version of condition 2. of the previous theorem is satisfied. For each countable subcollection $\{S_i \mid i=1,2,\ldots\}$ of $\mathfrak{S}$, we have $\bigcap \{\overline{S}_i \mid i=1,2,\ldots\} = \overline{\bigcap \{S_i \mid i=1,2,\ldots\}}$ ($\overline{}$ denoting the closure in $\upsilon(\mathfrak{S})X$).

PROOF. If $S = \bigcap \{S_i \mid i=1,2,\ldots\}$, then it is sufficient to prove that $\bigcap \{\overline{S}_i \mid i=1,2,\ldots\} \subset \overline{S}$. Let p be a point of $\bigcap \{\overline{S}_i \mid i=1,2,\ldots\}$ and suppose, on the contrary, that $p \notin \overline{S}$. According to the regularity condition of $\overline{\mathfrak{S}}$ there exist $T_1, \ldots, T_k \in \mathfrak{S}$ such that $p \in \bigcap \{\overline{T}_i \mid 1 \le i \le k\}$ and $\bigcap \{\overline{T}_i \mid 1 \le i \le k\} \cap \overline{S} = \emptyset$. Now, $\bigcap \{S_i \mid i=1,2,\ldots\} \cap \bigcap \{T_i \mid 1 \le i \le k\} = \emptyset$, but we do have $p \in \bigcap \{\overline{S}_i \mid i=1,2,\ldots\} \cap \bigcap \{\overline{T}_i \mid 1 \le i \le k\}$. This contradicts condition 2 of the previous theorem.

3. If the subbase $\mathfrak{S}$ satisfies the condition that each maximal centered family of members of $\mathfrak{S}$ with the countable intersection property has non empty intersection, then $\upsilon(\mathfrak{S})X = X$.

PROOF. Suppose, on the contrary, that $p \in \upsilon(\mathfrak{S})X \setminus X = Y \setminus X$. Define $\mathfrak{S}_1 \subset \mathfrak{S}$ by the condition $\mathfrak{S}_1 = \{S \in \mathfrak{S} \mid p \in \overline{S}\}$. According to condition 2. of the previous theorem, the collection $\mathfrak{S}_1$ is a prime centered system of members of $\mathfrak{S}$ with the countable intersection property.
Thus by 3.1.4. $\bigcap \mathfrak{S}_1 \neq \emptyset$. If $q \in \bigcap \mathfrak{S}_1$, then obviously $p \neq q$, and there exists $S \in \mathfrak{S}$ such that $p \in \overline{S}$ and $q \notin \overline{S}$. However, since $S \in \mathfrak{S}_1$, this contradicts $q \in \bigcap \mathfrak{S}_1$.

3.1.8. The third remark in 3.1.7. together with 3.1.4. yields the following intrinsic characterization of realcompactness.

THEOREM. A T_1-space X is a realcompact completely regular space if and only if there exists a closed subbase $\mathfrak{S}$ for its topology that satisfies the regularity, normality and countability conditions, and moreover satisfies the condition that each maximal centered family of members of $\mathfrak{S}$ with c.i.p. has non empty intersection.

REMARK. Under the hypotheses of the first three conditions, the latter is equivalent with X is $\aleph_1$-ultracompact relative to $\mathfrak{S}$.

3.1.9. If $\mathfrak{S}$ is a closed subbase for X, then $\mathfrak{S}$ satisfies the *strong regularity condition* iff each $S \in \mathfrak{S}$ and $x \notin S$ are screened by a cover of X consisting of two members of $\mathfrak{S}$. $\mathfrak{S}$ satisfies the *strong normality condition* iff each two disjoint members of $\mathfrak{S}$ are screened by a cover of X consisting of two members of $\mathfrak{S}$.

Note that if $\mathfrak{S}$ is a closed base and not only a subbase, then the conditions of strong regularity and strong normality of $\mathfrak{S}$ are equivalent to the conditions of base-regularity and base-normality introduced in Chapter II Section 2. Furthermore, note that the family of zerosets of a completely regular space is a closed (sub)base which satisfies the strong regularity and strong normality conditions.

The following theorem generalizes the result stating that a completely regular space is realcompact iff for each maximal centered family $\mathfrak{D}$ of cozerosets for which $\overline{\mathfrak{D}}$ has c.i.p., the intersection $\cap\,\overline{\mathfrak{D}}$ is non empty. See also theorems 2.1.2. and 2.2.8.

THEOREM. Let $\mathfrak{S}$ be a complemented [1] closed subbase for a space X which satisfies the strong regularity, strong normality, and countability conditions. Denote by $\mathfrak{U}$ the collection $\{X \setminus S \mid S \in \mathfrak{S}\}$. Then the following statements are equivalent:

1. For each maximal centered system $\mathfrak{U}_1$ of members of $\mathfrak{U}$ for which $\overline{\mathfrak{U}}_1$ has the countable intersection property, we have $\cap\,\overline{\mathfrak{U}}_1 \neq \emptyset$.

---

[1] A subbase $\mathfrak{S}$ is called *complemented* if $S \in \mathfrak{S}$ implies $\overline{X \setminus S} \in \mathfrak{S}$.

2. Each maximal centered system of members of $\mathfrak{S}$ which satisfies the countable intersection property has non empty intersection.

PROOF. 1 $\Longrightarrow$ 2. Let $Y = \upsilon(\mathfrak{S})X$ be the realcompactification of X described above. It is enough to show that $Y = X$, whence it follows from 3.1.7. Remark 3 that $\mathfrak{S}$ satisfies condition 2. Suppose, on the contrary, that $p \in Y \setminus X$. Let $\mathfrak{U}_1$ be the subcollection of $\mathfrak{U}$ consisting of those sets U for which $p \in \overline{U}^Y$. If U is some member of $\mathfrak{U}$ which intersects each finite subcollection of $\mathfrak{U}_1$ then each basic-neighborhood in Y of p of the form $\cap \{X \setminus \overline{S_i}^Y | i=1,2,\dots,n\}$ where $X \setminus S_i \in \mathfrak{U}_1$ for $i = 1, 2, \dots, n$, intersects U. Thus $p \in \overline{U}^Y$ proving that $\mathfrak{U}_1$ is a maximal centered system of members of $\mathfrak{U}$. If $\{U_i | i=1,2,\dots\}$ is a countable subcollection of $\mathfrak{U}_1$, then $\{\overline{U_i}^Y | i=1,2,\dots\}$ is a countable subcollection of $\overline{\mathfrak{S}}$ ($\mathfrak{S}$ is complemented). Thus from the special property of the realcompactification Y, we conclude that $\cap \{\overline{U_i}^X | i=1,2,\dots\} \neq \emptyset$. By assumption there exists a point q in $\cap \overline{\mathfrak{U}_1}^X$. Obviously $p \neq q$. Using the strong regularity condition of the subbase $\{\overline{S}^Y | S \in \mathfrak{S}\}$ of Y we can easily see that there exists $S \in \mathfrak{S}$ such that $p \in Y \setminus \overline{S}^Y$ while q is not in the closure in Y of $Y \setminus \overline{S}^Y$. Thus q is not in the closure in X of $X \setminus S$ since X is dense in Y. Hence, $\overline{X \setminus S}^X$ is a member of $\overline{\mathfrak{U}_1}^X$ which does not contain q. This is a contradiction, and it proves the first part of the theorem.

2 $\Longrightarrow$ 1. Let $\mathfrak{U}_1$ be a maximal centered system of members of $\mathfrak{U}$, and suppose that condition 1. is satisfied. Let $\mathfrak{F}$ be some ultrafilter in X which contains the collection $\mathfrak{U}_1$; we shall prove that $\mathfrak{F} \cap \mathfrak{S}$ satisfies the countable intersection property. Then by lemma 3.1.4., it follows that $\mathfrak{F}$ is convergent, and in particular it follows that $\cap \overline{\mathfrak{U}}_1 \neq \emptyset$. Let us suppose that $\{S_i | i=1,2,\dots\}$ is a countable subcollection of $\mathfrak{F} \cap \mathfrak{S}$ with empty intersection. Then the family $\{X \setminus S_i | i=1,2,\dots\}$ obviously is a countable cover of X which, by virtue of the countability condition for $\mathfrak{S}$, possesses a countable refinement $\mathfrak{T} = \{T_i | i=1,2,\dots\}$ by members of $\mathfrak{S}$. Since $\overline{\mathfrak{U}}_1$ satisfies the countable intersection property, there exists a natural number k such that T_k intersects each member of $\overline{\mathfrak{U}}_1$.

Select a natural number l such that $T_k \subset X \setminus S_l$. Since $\mathfrak{S}$ satisfies the strong normality condition, there exists S and $T \in \mathfrak{S}$ such that $T_k \subset T$, $S_l \subset S$, $T \cap S_l = \emptyset$, $S \cap T_k = \emptyset$, $S \cup T = X$. Obviously, $S_l \subset X \setminus T \in \mathfrak{U} \cap \mathfrak{J} = \mathfrak{U}_1$ and $\overline{X \setminus T} \cap T_k = \emptyset$. This, however, contradicts the fact that T_k intersects each member of $\overline{\mathfrak{U}}_1$. Thus the proof of the theorem is complete.

REMARK. Observe that in the proof of 2 $\Longrightarrow$ 1 we do not use that $\mathfrak{S}$ is complemented.

2. MAXIMALITY OF $\upsilon(\mathfrak{S})X$

3.2.1. The following theorem generalizes the result which states that a continuous map of a completely regular space X into a completely regular space Y has a continuous extension over the Hewitt realcompactifications of X and Y (cf. [10]).

THEOREM. Let X and Y be T_1-spaces, and suppose that $\mathfrak{S}$ and $\mathfrak{T}$ are closed subbases for X and Y, respectively, which satisfy the regularity, normality, and countability conditions. If f is a (continuous) map from X into Y with the property that $f^{-1}(T) \in \mathfrak{S}$ for each $T \in \mathfrak{T}$, then there exists a continuous extension f^* of f which carries $\upsilon(\mathfrak{S})X$ into $\upsilon(\mathfrak{T})Y$.

PROOF. If no confusion is possible, then we denote closures in $\upsilon(\mathfrak{S})X$ and $\upsilon(\mathfrak{T})Y$ by the symbol $\overline{}$.

Let p be an arbitrary point of $\upsilon(\mathfrak{S})X$. Denote by $\mathfrak{T}_1$ the subcollection of $\mathfrak{T}$ consisting of those sets T for which $p \in \overline{f^{-1}(T)}$. The collection $\overline{\mathfrak{T}}_1$ has the countable intersection property, for if $\{\overline{T}_i \mid i=1,2,\ldots\}$ is a countable subcollection of $\overline{\mathfrak{T}}_1$ and $\cap \{\overline{T}_i \mid i=1,2,\ldots\} = \emptyset$, then $\cap \{f^{-1}(T_i) \mid i=1,2,\ldots\} = \emptyset$. According to theorem 3.1.6. we also have $\cap \{\overline{f^{-1}(T_i)} \mid i=1,2,\ldots\} = \emptyset$, which is impossible since p must belong to this set. The centered system $\overline{\mathfrak{T}}_1$ is also a prime centered system. Indeed, if $\{\overline{T}_k | k=1,2,\ldots,n\}$ is a finite subcollection of $\overline{\mathfrak{T}}$ which is a cover of $\upsilon(\mathfrak{T})Y$, then the collection $\{\overline{f^{-1}(T_k)} | k=1,2,\ldots,n\}$ is a cover of $\upsilon(\mathfrak{S})X$. Hence, there exists j $(1 \le j \le n)$ such that $p \in \overline{f^{-1}(T_j)}$, and we have $\overline{T}_j \in \overline{\mathfrak{T}}_1$. By virtue of 3.1.4. and 3.1.6., we can define $f^*(p) = \cap \overline{\mathfrak{T}}_1$. The mapping $f^*: \upsilon(\mathfrak{S})X \to \upsilon(\mathfrak{T})Y$ is an extension of f, for if $p \in X$, then we have $f(p) \in \cap \{\overline{T} \in \overline{\mathfrak{T}} | p \in f^{-1}(T)\} = \cap \{\overline{T} \in \overline{\mathfrak{T}} | p \in \overline{f^{-1}(T)}\} = f^*(p)$. Therefore it remains to show that f^* is continuous. Let x be an arbitrary point of $\upsilon(\mathfrak{S})X$ such that $f^*(x) \in \upsilon(\mathfrak{T})Y$, and let T be some member of $\mathfrak{T}$ such that $f^*(x) \in \upsilon(\mathfrak{T})Y \setminus \overline{T}$. In order to prove the continuity of f^* it suffices to show that there exists a neighborhood of x which is mapped into $\upsilon(\mathfrak{T})Y \setminus \overline{T}$ by f^* (note that by 3.1.6, the collection $\{\upsilon(\mathfrak{T})Y \setminus \overline{T} | T \in \mathfrak{T}\}$ is a subbase for the open sets of $\upsilon(\mathfrak{T})Y$). Since $f^*(x) \notin \overline{T}$ there exists a decomposition of $\overline{T}$ into $G_1, \ldots, G_n$ such that each pair $(f^*(x), G_i)$ is screened by a finite cover $\{\overline{T}^i_1, \ldots, \overline{T}^i_{n(i)}\}$ of $\upsilon(\mathfrak{T})Y$ by members of $\overline{\mathfrak{T}}$. For each i, let $\overline{T}^i_j$, $j = 1, 2, \ldots, k(i)$ be the elements of this collection which do not intersect x.

Define

$$U = \cap \{\upsilon(\mathfrak{S})X \setminus \cup \{\overline{f^{-1}(T^i_j)} | 1 \le j \le k(i)\} | 1 \le i \le n\}.$$

Then U is a neighborhood of x which is mapped into $\upsilon(\mathfrak{T})Y \setminus \overline{T}$ by f^*. This completes the proof of the theorem.

3.2.2. An obvious modification of the proof of the foregoing theorem yields the following more general result (this generalizes a result of ENGELKING [4]):

THEOREM. Let X and Y be T_1-spaces and suppose that $\mathfrak{T}$ is a closed subbase of Y which satisfies the regularity, normality and countability conditions. If f is a continuous map from a dense subset Z of X into Y such that $\cap \{cl_X(f^{-1}(T_i)) | i=1,2,\ldots\} = \emptyset$ for each countable subcollection $\{T_i | i=1,2,\ldots\}$ of $\mathfrak{T}$ with empty intersection in Y, then

f has a continuous extension which carries X into $\upsilon(\mathfrak{T})Y$.

3.2.3. COROLLARY. Let X be a T_1-space and $\mathfrak{S}$ a closed subbase for X which satisfies the regularity, normality and countability conditions. The extension $\upsilon(\mathfrak{S})X$ of X which is constructed in theorem 3.1.6. is essentially unique in the sense that if $\mu(\mathfrak{S})X$ is any extension of X satisfying conditions 1. and 2. of 3.1.6., then there exists a homeomorphism of $\upsilon(\mathfrak{S})X$ onto $\mu(\mathfrak{S})X$ which leaves X pointwise fixed. Furthermore, we have $\mu(\mathfrak{S})X = X$ if and only if every maximal centered family of members of $\mathfrak{S}$ with c.i.p. has non empty intersection in X.

3.2.4. EXAMPLE. If X is a Lindelöf space, then for each closed subbase $\mathfrak{S}$ which satisfies the regularity, normality and countability conditions, we have $\upsilon(\mathfrak{S})X = X$. This statement does not generally hold in arbitrary realcompact spaces. Indeed, if X is a discrete space of cardinal $> \aleph_0$, then let $\mathfrak{S}$ be the collection of singleton points and complements of singleton points in X. It is easy to see that $\mathfrak{S}$ satisfies all conditions required and $\upsilon(\mathfrak{S})X$ is homeomorphic with the one point compactification of X.

3.2.5. THEOREM. Let $\{X_\alpha \mid \alpha \in A\}$ be a collection of topological spaces and $X = \Pi\{X_\alpha \mid \alpha \in A\}$. Suppose that for $\alpha \in A$, $\mathfrak{S}_\alpha$ is a closed subbase for X_α which satisfies the regularity, normality and countability conditions.
Then the collection $\mathfrak{S}$ consisting of the sets $\pi_\alpha^{-1}(C)$, where π_α is the natural projection onto the α'th coordinate space and C a member of $\mathfrak{S}_\alpha$, is a closed subbase for X which satisfies the regularity, normality and countability conditions. Furthermore, $\Pi\{\upsilon(\mathfrak{S}_\alpha)X_\alpha \mid \alpha \in A\}$ is homeomorphic with $\upsilon(\mathfrak{S})X$ [1].

PROOF. One easily verifies that $\mathfrak{S}$ is a closed subbase for X which satisfies the regularity, normality and countability conditions.

---

1) In fact we prove even more, namely, that there exists a homeomorphism which leaves X pointwise fixed.

By 3.2.1., for each $\alpha \in A$, there exists a continuous extension π^*_α of π_α which carries $\upsilon(\mathfrak{S})X$ into $\upsilon(\mathfrak{S}_\alpha)X_\alpha$. Define $i^*: \upsilon(\mathfrak{S})X \to \Pi\{\upsilon(\mathfrak{S}_\alpha)X_\alpha | \alpha \in A\}$ by the conditions $(i^*(x))_\alpha = \pi^*_\alpha(x)$ $(\alpha \in A)$. Theorem 3.2.2. gives a method to extend the inclusion map j of X into $\upsilon(\mathfrak{S})X$ to a continuous mapping $j^*: \Pi\{\upsilon(\mathfrak{S}_\alpha)X_\alpha | \alpha \in A\} \to \upsilon(\mathfrak{S})X$. The composition map $j^* \circ i^*$ has the property that it leaves the dense set X pointwise fixed. Consequently $j^* \circ i^*$ is the identity map of $\upsilon(\mathfrak{S})X$. By applying the same argument to $i^* \circ j^*$ the theorem now follows.

3. GENERALIZED LINDELÖF SPACES

3.3.1. Let $\mathfrak{S}$ be a subbase for the closed sets of a topological space X. $\mathfrak{S}$ is called a *Lindelöf subbase* for X if it has the following properties:

1. $\mathfrak{S}$ satisfies the strong regularity condition
2. $\mathfrak{S}$ satisfies the normality condition
3. Each centered family of members of $\mathfrak{S}$ with the countable intersection property has non empty intersection.

A space X is called a *generalized Lindelöf space* provided that there exists a Lindelöf subbase for its closed sets.

3.3.2. THEOREM. a) Every regular Lindelöf space is a generalized Lindelöf space, b) every topological product of generalized Lindelöf spaces is a generalized Lindelöf space, c) every discrete space of cardinal $\leq \aleph$ is a generalized Lindelöf space.

PROOF. a). If X is a regular Lindelöf space, then the family of all closed subsets and the family of all zerosets are examples of Lindelöf subbases for X. Thus X is a generalized Lindelöf space.

b). Suppose that $\{X_\alpha | \alpha \in A\}$ is a collection of generalized Lindelöf

spaces and $X = \Pi\{X_\alpha | \alpha \in A\}$. For $\alpha \in A$, let $\mathfrak{S}_\alpha$ be a Lindelöf subbase for X_α and let $\mathfrak{S}$ be the subbase for X consisting of all sets of the form $\pi_\alpha^{-1}(C)$, where π_α is the natural projection into the α'th coordinate space and C a member of $\mathfrak{S}_\alpha$. It is easy to see that $\mathfrak{S}$ satisfies conditions 1. and 2. Now, let $\mathfrak{S}'$ be a subcollection of $\mathfrak{S}$ with the countable intersection property; we will show that $\cap \mathfrak{S}' \neq \emptyset$. For $\alpha \in A$, let $\mathfrak{S}'_\alpha$ be the subcollection of $\mathfrak{S}_\alpha$ consisting of the sets $\pi_\alpha S$ for which $S \in \mathfrak{S}'$.
It is easy to see that $\mathfrak{S}'_\alpha$ satisfies the countable intersection property and, by assumption, there exists $p_\alpha \in \cap \mathfrak{S}'_\alpha$ for each $\alpha \in A$. The point p of X whose α'th coordinate is p_α is in the intersection of $\mathfrak{S}'$.
c). Let D be a discrete space of cardinal $\leq \aleph$, we may suppose that D is a subset of the real numbers. If $\mathfrak{S}$ is the collection of subsets of the form $\{x \in D | x > a\}$, $\{x \in D | x < a\}$, $\{x \in D | x \geq a\}$, $\{x \in D | x \leq a\}$ $(a \in R)$, then $\mathfrak{S}$ is a Lindelöf subbase for the space D.

3.3.3. THEOREM. Every generalized Lindelöf space is a realcompact completely regular space.

PROOF. Let $\mathfrak{S}$ be a Lindelöf subbase for the closed sets of a space X. It is obvious that $\mathfrak{S}$ satisfies the regularity and normality conditions, hence X is completely regular by 3.1.2. We shall prove that $\mathfrak{S}$ satisfies the countability condition, whence it follows from 3.1.8. that X is realcompact. Let $\{X \setminus S_i | i=1,2,\ldots\}$ be a countable cover of X and suppose that $S_i \in \mathfrak{S}$ for $i = 1, 2, \ldots$. For fixed $i = 1, 2, \ldots$ and for each p, let $\{S_p^i, T_p^i\}$ be a two element cover of X by members of $\mathfrak{S}$ which screens p and S_i. The collection $\{X \setminus T_p^i | p \in X\}$ is an open cover of X which has a countable subcover $\{X \setminus T_{pn}^i | n=1,2,\ldots\}$ (Using the dual of 3. of the definition of Lindelöf subbase). The collection $\{S_{pn}^i | i,n=1,2,\ldots\}$ is a countable refinement of $\{X \setminus S_i | i=1,2,\ldots\}$ and consists of members of $\mathfrak{S}$.

3.3.4. THEOREM. Let X be a countably paracompact normal space and suppose that there exists a subbase $\mathfrak{S}$ for the closed sets which satisfies only the condition that every maximal centered system of members of $\mathfrak{S}$ satisfying c.i.p. has non empty intersection. Then X is realcompact.

PROOF. This is obvious from 2.2.3. and 2.2.8.

PROBLEM. The foregoing theorems in this section show that most of our known realcompact spaces are also generalized Lindelöf spaces. Professor de Groot has raised the question whether *every* realcompact completely regular space is a generalized Lindelöf space. Up to the present we have not succeeded in solving this problem and thus in generalizing theorem 3.1.8.

REFERENCES

1. J.M. AARTS, Dimension and Deficiency in General Topology, Thesis, Univ. Amsterdam, 1966.

2. R.A. ALO and H.L. SHAPIRO, Z-realcompactifications and normal bases, issued for publication.

3. B. BANASCHEWSKI, Über nulldimensionale Räume, Math. Nachr. 13, 129-140 (1955).

4. R. ENGELKING, Remarks on realcompact spaces, Fund. Math. 55, 303-308.

5. R. ENGELKING and S. MROWKA, On E-compact spaces, Bull. Acad. Pol. Sci. Ser. Math. Astro Phys. 6, 429-436 (1958).

6. P. FREYD, Abelian categories, Harper and Row, New York, 1964.

7. O. FRINK, Compactifications and seminormal spaces, Am. J. Math. 86, 602-607 (1964).

8. Zd. FROLIK, Baire spaces and some generalizations of complete metric spaces, Czech. Math. Journ. Vol. 11, 237-248 (1961).

9. Zd. FROLIK, A generalization of realcompact spaces, Czech. Math. Journ. Vol. 13, 127-138 (1963).

10. L. GILLMAN and M. JERISON, Rings of continuous functions, van Nostrand, Princeton, 1960.

11. J. DE GROOT, Subcompactness and the Baire Category theorem, Indag. Math., 25 N° 5 (1963).

12. J. DE GROOT and J.M. AARTS, Syllabus Colloquium Cotopology 1964-1965, Math. Centrum, Amsterdam, 1966.

13. J. DE GROOT and J.M. AARTS, Complete regularity as a separation axiom, to appear in Canad. Journ. Math.

14. H. HERRLICH, Fortsetzbarkeit stetiger Abbildungen und Kompaktheidsgrad topologischer Räume, Math. Zeitschr. 96, 64-72 (1967).

15. H. HERRLICH, $\mathfrak{E}$ -kompakte Räume, Math. Zeitschr. 96, 228-255 (1967).

16. H. HERRLICH, On the concept of reflection in General Topology, issued for publication.

17. H. HERRLICH and J. VAN DER SLOT, Properties which are closely related to compactness, Indag. Math., 29, N° 5, 524-530 (1967).

18. M. HENRIKSEN and J.R. ISBELL, Some properties of compactifications, Duke Math. Journ. 25 (1958).

19. E. HEWITT, Rings of real-valued continuous functions, Trans. Am. Math. Soc. 64, 54-99 (1948).

20. M. HUŠEK Remarks on reflections, Comm. Math. Univ. Carol. 7, 249-259 (1966).

21. J.R. ISBELL, Uniform spaces, Am. Math. Soc., Providence, 1964.

22. T. ISIWATA, Mappings and spaces, Pac. Journ. of Math. 20, 3 (1967).

23. J.L. KELLEY, General Topology, van Nostrand, Princeton, 1955.

24. J.F. KENNISON, Reflective functors in general topology and elsewhere, Trans. Am. Math. Soc. 118, 303-315 (1965).

25. S. MROWKA, A property of Hewitt extension υX of topological spaces, Bull. Acad. Polon. Sci. Ser. Math. Astro Phys. 6, 95-96 (1958).

26. J. NAGATA, Modern Dimension theory, Noordhoff, Groningen, 1965.

27. J. NAGATA, Modern general topology, Noordhoff, Groningen, 1968.

28. J. VAN DER SLOT, Nuldimensionale metrische ruimten, scriptie, Univ. of Amsterdam, 1966.

29. J. VAN DER SLOT, Universal topological properties, ZW 1966-011, Math. Centrum, Amsterdam, 1966.

30. G.E. STRECKER, Cotopologies and generalized compactness conditions, Doct. diss., Tulane University, 1966.

31. E.F. STEINER, Normal families and completely regular spaces, Duke Math. Journ. 33, 743-745 (1966).